30-SECOND
FORENSIC SCIENCE

30-SECOND
FORENSIC SCIENCE

The 50 key topics revealing
criminal investigation from
behind the scenes

Editors
Sue Black & Niamh Nic Daéid

Foreword by
Val McDermid

Contributors
Mike Allen, Sue Black
Christophe Champod
Niamh Nic Daéid
Lorna Dawson, Zeno Geradts
Lucina Hackman
Adrian Linacre, Craig McKenzie
Paul Reedy, Chris Rynn
Diana Swales, Grant Thomson

Illustrator
Nicky Ackland-Snow

IVY PRESS

First published in the UK in 2018 by
Ivy Press
An imprint of The Quarto Group
The Old Brewery, 6 Blundell Street
London N7 9BH, United Kingdom
T (0)20 7700 6700 **F** (0)20 7700 8066
www.QuartoKnows.com

British Library Cataloguing-in-
Publication Data
A catalogue record for this
book is available from the
British Library.

ISBN: 978-1-78240-551-1

This book was conceived,
designed and produced by
Ivy Press
58 West Street, Brighton BN1 2RA, UK

Publisher **Susan Kelly**
Creative Director **Michael Whitehead**
Editorial Director **Tom Kitch**
Art Director **James Lawrence**
Commissioning Editor **Stephanie Evans**
Assistant Editor **Jenny Campbell**
Designer **Ginny Zeal**
Illustrator **Nicky Ackland-Snow**
Picture Researcher **Katie Greenwood**

Cover images Shutterstock/La Gorda

Typeset in Section

Printed in China

10 9 8 7 6 5 4 3 2

Dedication

It is rare to find a senior judge who is
so openly supportive of forensic science
and so it is an honour and a personal
pleasure for us to dedicate this text to
the recently retired Lord Chief Justice
of England and Wales, The Rt Hon. the
Lord Thomas of Cwmgiedd.

CONTENTS

FOREWORD

Val McDermid

I've been writing crime fiction for over thirty years, and in that time I've witnessed a revolution in the effectiveness of forensic science in bringing complex criminal cases to successful conclusions. But, like most people, what I've also seen are hundreds of dramatic and literary versions of forensic science that are, frankly, science fiction. In TV shows and films and – I'm sorry to say – far too many crime novels, the discipline is portrayed with sometimes shocking inaccuracy.

Succinct though it is, this informative guide will correct assumptions, explain the reality and share with you some of the extraordinary ways that science has been brought to the service of the courts. And I promise you, it will fill your head with wonder.

Although I write fiction, I try to bring authenticity to my work, and one of the ways I achieve this is by picking the brains of a diverse range of forensic scientists. They're invariably generous with their time and their expertise. I generally turn up with half a dozen questions and I leave with the answers to them all and a host of other things I never thought to ask. The scientists I work with are good communicators who know how to explain complex procedures in terms that lay people can understand. I once asked what a body would look like after 200 years in a peat bog. 'A leather bag with a face on,' came the almost instantaneous reply.

There have been a lot of 'Wow!' moments along the way for me in my encounters with the forensic investigators. You'll find some of them in the pages of this book – the chemical luminol can detect blood in one part per million; blood leaves the body in the form of a ball; the dead insects plastered across your car can reveal exactly where you've been; and forensic botanists can match a seed pod on a suspect's clothing to a specific tree.

But you'll also find clear and concise explanations of the many disciplines whose practitioners work together to do their best to ensure that the questions thrown up by criminal acts are answered satisfactorily.

In death as in life, the human body is an amazing repository of information, and you couldn't have better guides to decoding its secrets than this pair of professors. Sue Black is a forensic anthropologist. She knows how to unravel your biological and your personal identity. She brings the dead home to their loved ones. Niamh Nic Daéid is a forensic chemist; there is very little she doesn't know about fire, explosives and drugs. The combination of their two sets of skills might seem odd but what they have in common is a symbiotic understanding of the importance of the chemical and biological reactions they witness. What Sue and Niamh have done for us here is to crack open the door into their investigative world and I suspect it's a door few of us will resist opening wider.

Dear reader, prepare to be amazed.

Blood patterns can be analysed to determine movements of the victim and their attacker. Any evidence gathered at the scene of a crime confirms the observation of Dr Edmond Locard, popularly known as the Sherlock Holmes of France, that 'every contact leaves a trace.'

INTRODUCTION
Sue Black & Niamh Nic Daéid

Collectively we have been embroiled in the business of forensic science for over half a century. We have sufficient longevity in our corporate memory to have witnessed trends come and go, reputations rise and fall, and watch the confidence in our science wax and wane. What never seems to diminish though, is the public's insatiable appetite for forensic science, the investigator's zeal for its value and the court's reliance on its ability to help a jury reach a verdict that best serves justice.

It is always a challenge to look back into history to try to decide when a particular branch of science was first conceived or used to best effect. Many of our more traditional aspects of forensic science find themselves being formalized at the end of the nineteenth century – fingerprints, handwriting examination, ballistics, biometrics and shoe patterns. Then in the mid-1980s the world of forensic science was turned on its head when Sir Alec Jeffreys discovered the variation that exists within our DNA and how that can be used to establish a level of certainty in identity. Virtually overnight, forensic science was split into two eras – pre and post 1984 – an interesting date in relation to George Orwell's dystopian novel.

The great secret is that forensic science is a misnomer as there is no such single discipline. It is in reality a discipline of scientific disciplines and is a blanket term used to refer to those sciences utilized by the justice system and bound together in a singular desire to interpret and evaluate information within a framework of specific case circumstances. Within that classification the subjects of mechanical engineering and anatomy have as much right to be included as do the more readily recognized subjects of toxicology and DNA. Certain aspects of biology, chemistry, physics and mathematics appear in the courtrooms more frequently than others and as a result, they have collectively acquired the term 'forensic science'. The overriding purpose of introducing science into the courtroom is to help the jury to reach a safe verdict in the pursuit of justice.

Remarkable and relatively recent advances in human molecular genetics mean that almost every individual in the world can be distinguished from another, even if they are allegedly identical twins.

Our first task for this book was to select 50 evidence types that would serve as an introduction to the subject. At a meeting within the Royal Society in London in 2015 we had asked our community of scientists and judges which evidence types they encountered most frequently within their daily work and they helpfully suggested a list of over 40. We have chosen to represent these in this book with the full realization that we could have doubled this number quite easily. This conveys the enormity and diversity of the relationship between science and the law as it applies not only to justice but also to liberty and, in parts of the world where the death penalty exists, forensic science can impact on a person's life.

This book is divided into seven chapters and each opens with a glossary of terms and includes the profile of a person who was or is preeminent in the field. The first chapter, **The Body**, considers the impact of the human body in forensic science through different disciplines including pathology, anthropology, odontology and radiology. The second, **Biometrics**, explores those characteristics that can be used to establish identity. It naturally leads with DNA and is followed by the well-known disciplines of fingerprinting, facial analysis and handwriting along with others. The third chapter, **Traces**, introduces evidence where even minute volumes of identified material can be critical to the investigation of crime. The value of fibre analysis, glass, paint or gunshot residue is considered and Locard's principle of exchange of trace material on contact is re-stated. Then follows **Physical & Chemical Analysis**, which considers those aspects of forensic science that are more rooted in the physical sciences including toolmark, blood and toxicological analysis. Chapter 5 addresses evidence that originates from **Natural Sciences** including pollen, soil, insects and other wildlife. Our modern world is heavily reliant on digital technology and so **Digital Records** delves lightly into the realms of image analysis and cyber-crime. **The Law & Science** concludes where all forensic science must eventually serve its purpose – in the courtroom. We discuss expert witnesses, legal admissibility and the interpretation and presentation of evidence within our judicial systems.

The historical and contemporary value of forensic science to society is clear and apparent. If you wish to learn more about this most fascinating and absorbing discipline of disciplines, this book is an ideal place to start. As Sherlock Holmes so aptly conveyed 'the little things are infinitely the most important.'

Forensic laboratories routinely analyse seizures of herbal substances and unknown powders, liquids and tablets to determine whether they contain illegal drugs.

THE BODY

THE BODY
GLOSSARY

aggravated homicide When the murder incorporates some specific circumstances such as the intentional killing of a child or a serving police officer, or terminating a pregnancy etc.

angiography The analysis of specialized X-ray images that allow blood vessels to be visualized.

algor mortis The second stage of death, represented by the change in body temperature, until the ambient temperature is matched. *See also* perimortem and rigor mortis.

antemortem Literally meaning 'before death'. *See also* post-mortem.

average soft tissue depths (ASTDs) The thickness of the soft tissues of the face that lie over the bones of the skull.

cadaver A dead body or a corpse.

dentition The arrangement, number and type of teeth in a particular species.

entomology The scientific study of insects.

exsanguination The draining of blood.

Geomagic Freeform haptic-feedback virtual-sculpture system A three-dimensional engineering tool used in forensic facial reconstruction that provides genuine three-dimensional navigation that integrates a sense of touch.

histology The microscopic structure of tissues.

International Criminal Police Organization (INTERPOL) An intergovernmental organization founded in 1923 that facilitates international police cooperation.

livor mortis Discoloration of skin due to the pooling of blood after death.

multislice spiral CT A specialized form of computed tomography that improves the resulting three-dimensional image.

odontology The study of the structure and disease of teeth.

pathologist A medical practitioner concerned with the diagnosis of disease.

perimortem Literally means 'around the time of death'.

post-mortem Literally meaning 'after death'. *See also* antemortem.

R v In the titles of British legal cases, *R* is used to denote that the case has been brought by the Crown. Therefore, in the reign of a King this stands for Rex or in the reign of a Queen it stands for Regina. (The 'v' stands for 'versus'.)

rigor mortis The stiffening of the body after death. *See also* algor mortis.

toxicology The study of the adverse effects of chemicals and poisons on living organisms.

ultrasound A medical imaging technique that uses sound waves to produce pictures of the inside of the body.

Virtopsy® A virtual autopsy performed through the examination only of clinical images, for example CT (computed tomography) scans. Devised in the University of Bern, Switzerland.

AUTOPSY

the 30-second scenario

The term 'autopsy' derives from the Greek and refers to an eyewitness account or personal observation. It is most frequently associated with the world of forensic/legal medicine and represents a thorough external and internal examination of the deceased to establish specific facts to the satisfaction of a legal authority. It is usually performed by a medically qualified expert who is often referred to as a pathologist or medical examiner. The purpose of the autopsy is primarily to establish how the person died, why they died and their identity. How they died relates to the manner of their death, which might be due to a road-traffic accident or a gun-shot injury. Why they died relates to the specific reason that life ceased, which might be a myocardial infarction (heart attack) or transection of a major blood vessel and subsequent exsanguination (blood loss). Who the person was is usually only relevant to forensic investigations when human remains are found unexpectedly and there is no obvious evidence as to who the person was during life. The autopsy may require other areas of specialized investigation to help to answer the questions posed and may include toxicology, odontology, DNA analysis, fingerprinting or anthropology.

3-SECOND BIOGRAPHY
GIOVANNI MORGAGNI
1682–1771
Italian anatomist of the
Renaissance period who,
in his 80th year, completed
a five-volume treatise on
pathology – *De Sedibus
et Causis Morborum per
Anatomen Indagatis* ('The
seats and causes of diseases
investigated by anatomy')

30-SECOND TEXT
Sue Black

*The autopsy usually
permits qualified
experts to examine the
inside and outside of a
body to establish how
and why a person died.*

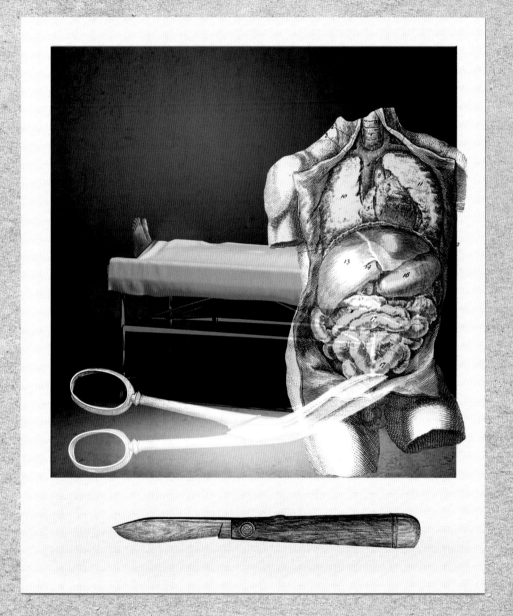

FORENSIC ANTHROPOLOGY

the 30-second scenario

Forensic anthropology is a branch of anthropology in which practitioners specialize in an understanding of the human skeleton. They apply methods of analysis to establish the biological identity of the deceased when remains are found but the name of the person is not known. This biological profile includes assessing the ancestral origin of the individual, age at death, sex and stature of the individual, plus additional detail, which may include previous fractures, disease or surgical procedures that will help to identify who the person may have been in life. The information is passed to an enquiry team who will search missing persons records in an attempt to find a match for the identity of the deceased. Forensic anthropologists also assist with the analysis of trauma found on the bones, which may include cut marks or injury to the bone that occurred at or around the time of death – known as perimortem trauma. They are able to distinguish between this and damage that has occurred to the body since death – or post-mortem damage. This can include marks of scavenging by animals, changes caused by exposure to roots, which leave etched marks on the bone surface, or to the weather where the bone surface starts to crack and splinter. Forensic anthropologists may also help identify human remains, especially after mass disasters that involve explosions or fires where bodies can be extremely fragmented.

RELATED TOPICS
See also
TIME DEATH INTERVAL
page 26

DISMEMBERMENT
page 30

TRAUMA
page 28

FORENSIC ARCHAEOLOGY
page 110

3-SECOND CLUE
Forensic anthropology involves the analysis of human skeletal remains to assist with the identification of an individual and an understanding of the cause of death.

3-MINUTE EVIDENCE
It is not always the deceased that requires identification to be established. Age estimation in the living is also undertaken by a forensic anthropologist when a juvenile presents to a court or to a border crossing with no formal documentation and their age needs to be established if they are to be processed appropriately by the authorities. In such a situation, age is usually established from changes to the skeleton that are visible through the use of medical imaging such as X-ray, MRI or CT.

3-SECOND BIOGRAPHY
CLYDE SNOW
1928–2014
American forensic anthropologist who was hugely influential in the development of forensic anthropology as a discipline. A founder of the Physical Anthropology section in the American Academy of Forensic Sciences (AAFS), Snow undertook both forensic and humanitarian work identifying those who had fallen victim to genocide and other atrocities in Argentina and the former Yugoslavia

30-SECOND TEXT
Lucina Hackman

Sex can be determined with greatest accuracy from the region of the pelvis.

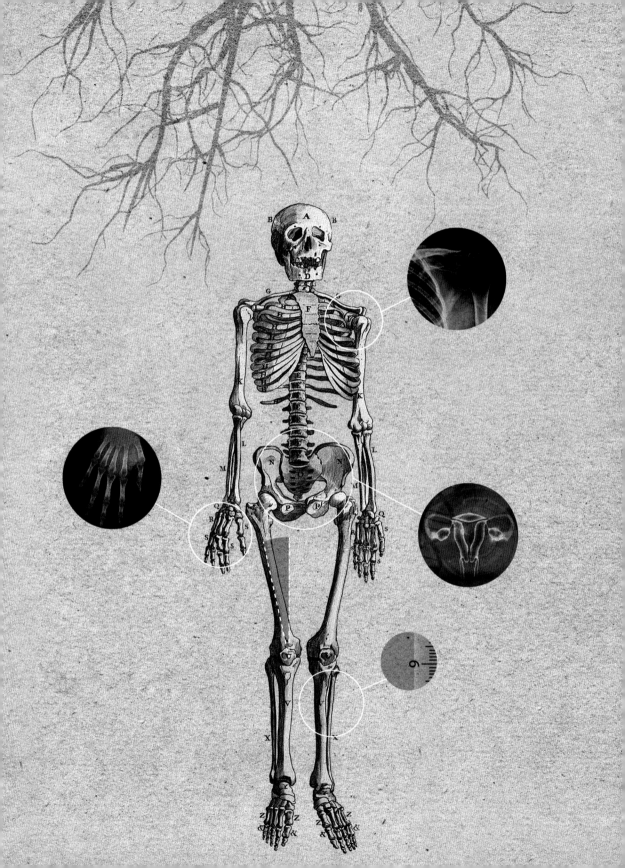

DENTAL RECORDS

the 30-second scenario

In humans, deciduous or baby teeth erupt into the mouth between six months and five years of age. At around six years, the first permanent teeth start to appear and a mixed stage of dentition will last until around the age of 12 when only permanent teeth remain. Dentists record the teeth present in the mouth, those that are absent, and those deformed or misaligned or that have been modified or restored perhaps by fillings, root canals or being covered with veneers. These records are primarily used for clinical purposes but may also be studied by a forensic odontologist when identification of a deceased needs to be established following a mass fatality event or the unexpected discovery of human remains. In the murder of Dr George Parkman, in Massachusetts in 1849, identification was in part achieved through the matching of artificial porcelain teeth that were constructed by his dentist, Dr Keep. In the infamous acid bath murders of the 1940s in Britain, John Haigh failed to realize that teeth could be used to identify his victims even following attempts to dissolve them with industrial-strength sulphuric acid. Teeth can survive explosions, fires or long periods buried in the ground. INTERPOL (International Criminal Police Organization) recognizes three primary identifiers – dentition, DNA and fingerprints.

3-SECOND CLUE
Forensic dentists, also known as odontologists, use information from dental records to assist in establishing the identity of an unknown deceased.

3-MINUTE EVIDENCE
In mass fatality events, the forensic odontologist will work in a mortuary to record the dentition of the deceased. A second odontologist will collect antemortem records from the dentists of people who have been reported missing by family or friends. In a matching centre, these two sets of information will be compared to establish if a match has been achieved and the deceased can then be named and the body released to family.

RELATED TOPICS
See also
AUTOPSY
page 14

FACIAL RECONSTRUCTION
page 24

FINGERPRINT ANALYSIS
page 38

3-SECOND BIOGRAPHY
NATHAN COOLEY KEEP
1800–75
Initially apprenticed to a jeweller, Keep went on to study and practise dentistry at Harvard. He gave critical evidence at the trial of the infamous murder of George Parkman in 1850, when John Webster was subsequently convicted and hanged. Dr Keep was credited with being one of the first dentists to develop porcelain teeth

30-SECOND TEXT
Sue Black

Human teeth can be used to establish the age (in children) as well as identification of a person.

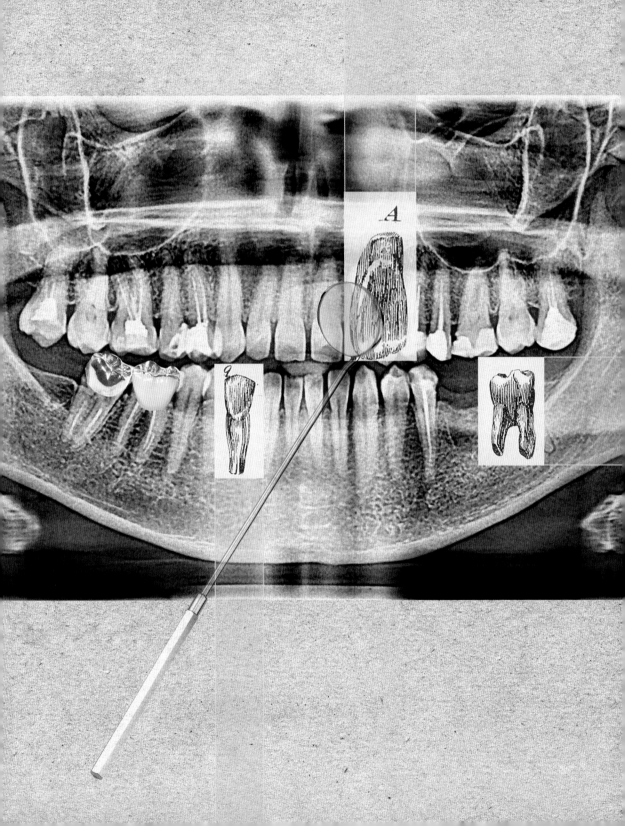

1877
Born in Leamington Spa, Warwickshire, UK

1905
Graduates MBChB from Magdalen College, Oxford, and becomes resident assistant pathologist at St Mary's Hospital, London

1908
Marries Edith Horton with whom he has four children

1910
R v Hawley Harvey Crippen

1915
R v George Joseph Smith – Brides in the Bath Murders

1922
R v Herbert Rowse Armstrong

1923
Knighted following his testimony in the Armstrong case

1924
Develops the 'murder bag' with Scotland Yard

1924
R v Patrick Mahon – Crumbles Murders

1927
R v John Robinson – Charing Cross Trunk Murder

1930
R v Alfred Rouse – Blazing Car Murder

1934
R v Mancini – Brighton Trunk Murder

1939
Advises MI5 on Operation Mincemeat

1947
Commits suicide by gas in his laboratory at University College, London

SIR BERNARD SPILSBURY

Sir Bernard Spilsbury graduated from Oxford with a degree in Medicine but although he had a fearsome work ethic, he was no intellectual. The theatre of the witness box offered him a platform where his irresistible and flamboyant personality could dominate. He cut a striking figure in his top hat, tails, spats and signature red-carnation buttonhole. He was unshakeable in his convictions and had the rare ability to convey difficult technical language into explanations the jury could understand – the people's pathologist. However, the judiciary became uneasy at what was being referred to as the 'Spilsbury effect', where his presence alone could sway the jury more than the evidence itself.

His earliest success came with the trial of Hawley Crippen, an American homeopath and medicine dispenser. When Crippen's wife, Cora, disappeared in January 1910, searches of their house led to the discovery of a torso under the brick floor of the basement. Spilsbury confirmed the body was Cora from an alleged abdominal scar on a piece of skin. Crippen was found guilty of murder and hanged in Pentonville Prison.

Spilsbury also led evidence against the English solicitor Herbert Armstrong who was accused of the attempted murder of his business rival and found guilty of the murder of his wife, Kitty Armstrong, both by arsenic poisoning. It was shortly after the success of this case that Spilsbury was knighted in 1923.

In conjunction with Scotland Yard, Spilsbury was responsible for the invention of the 'murder bag' – a forensic kit supplied to detectives that contained gloves, tweezers, evidence bags, a magnifying glass, compass, ruler and swabs.

Spilsbury was also integral to the success of Operation Mincemeat, a British disinformation strategy deployed during the Second World War intended to conceal the allied invasion of Sicily. It involved an identity swap with the corpse of a tramp disguised as Captain William Martin complete with planted fake documents. The body was released by submarine close to the southern coast of Spain and, when found, the fake documents fooled German intelligence. In response, enemy reinforcements were shifted to Greece and Sardinia leaving Sicily ripe for invasion.

Spilsbury's health declined following the death of his sons and his mistress in the 1940s. He was estranged from his wife and his finances were bleak. He was aware of increasing dementia and was crippled with arthritis. On 17 December 1947 he exchanged Christmas gifts with his staff, ate alone and then committed suicide by gas in his laboratory. Few attended his funeral.

Sue Black

MEDICAL IMAGING

the 30-second scenario

Medical imaging uses either ionizing radiation, for example radiography (X-ray) and computer tomography (CT), or non-ionizing radiation, for example magnetic resonance imaging (MRI) or ultrasound (US). Radiography has long been used to assist post-mortem examinations but the three-dimensional capability of CT and MRI has allowed the process of non-invasive autopsies to flourish. The term 'digital autopsy' entered our vocabulary in the 1980s and is used to augment, and intended to replace, the traditional autopsy. It has been largely accepted by communities who, on moral or religious grounds, view the traditional autopsy as desecration of the body. The digital autopsy attempts to answer the same investigative questions without physical dissection. For example, when assessing trauma, the three-dimensional visualization of a comminuted fracture (a break or splinter into more than two fragments), the trajectory of a projectile or the position of a foreign object may be lost once the body is disrupted. Further, the image can be stored and re-examined long after the body is buried or cremated, making it a long-term repository of evidence for future interrogation. However, the digital autopsy remains slightly contentious with some researchers suggesting that about 68 per cent accuracy is achieved when compared to the conventional standard autopsy approach in assessing a cause of death.

3-SECOND CLUE
Relatively recently, medical imaging has been extended into the field of forensic investigation as a non-invasive tool to assist in medico-legal autopsy procedures.

3-MINUTE EVIDENCE
The digital autopsy cannot yet replace fully the standard invasive approach of a traditional autopsy. However, with continued research and the inclusion of angiography (visualizing blood vessels), multislice spiral CT and MRI, surface scanning and multi-functional robotics for contamination-free sampling, medical imaging developments may yet herald the demise of the traditional autopsy. Work is also taking place that matches images of weapons to injuries whether in relation to hard tissues (dismemberment) or soft tissues (strangulation).

RELATED TOPICS
See also
AUTOPSY
page 14

TRAUMA
page 28

DISMEMBERMENT
page 30

3-SECOND BIOGRAPHY
RICHARD DIRNHOFER
1942–
Court physician who studied medicine at the University of Innsbruck and was Director of the Institute of Legal Medicine at the University of Bern, Switzerland, until 1991. He was the founder of the Virtopsy® trademark, which has led the way in digital autopsies since the 1980s

30-SECOND TEXT
Sue Black

Wilhelm Conrad Röntgen produced the first X-ray image in 1895, of his wife's hand. Because it is non-destructive, the X-ray is used widely as an analytical tool in forensic science.

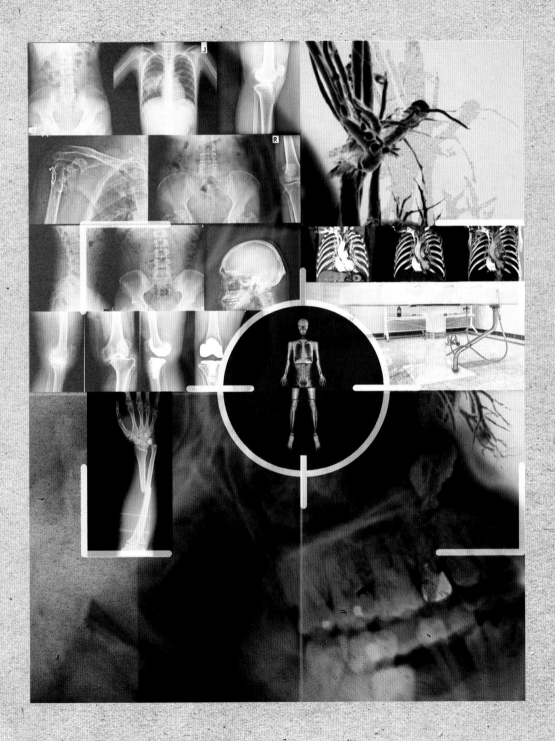

FACIAL RECONSTRUCTION

the 30-second scenario

Estimating and reconstructing facial features from a skull is a useful method for generating investigative leads if the four primary methods of identification (DNA, fingerprint or dental or x-ray match) are unsuccessful. This may have arisen because the unidentified individual was not included on a searchable database, or the body has decomposed past the point of data recovery. Facial reconstruction, or approximation, involves three aspects: average soft tissue depths (ASTDs), facial feature estimation methods and sculptural reconstruction of the musculature. The closest ASTDs might be from a different population (as the origin of the individual may not be known), so are only used as a guide. The muscles are sculpted to fit the individual skull, overruling the average measurements wherever there is contradiction. The bony orbits indicate whether the eyes are deep-set or protruding, upturned or downturned. The nose is estimated directly from the bony nasal aperture: in size, shape and asymmetry. Dental pattern dictates the width of the mouth and shape of the lips. All we can tell about ears from the skull is the general size and protrusion, but overall, this can be enough information to depict a face that is sufficiently similar in appearance to be recognized by a friend or family member of a missing person.

3-SECOND CLUE
Forensic facial reconstruction entails the approximation of facial anatomy from skull shape to facilitate the identification of decomposed or skeletonized human remains.

3-MINUTE EVIDENCE
Post-mortem depiction is a similar process, but instead of the skull, photographs of the face taken in the mortuary are used to create an image of how the person most likely appeared in life. Craniofacial super-imposition is a method in which a three-dimensional skull is aligned to a photo of a missing person, to compare them anatomically. This is only one of the methods that could be used to legally identify an individual from their skull.

RELATED TOPIC
See also
DENTAL RECORDS
page 18

3-SECOND BIOGRAPHIES
WILTON MARION KROGMAN
1903–87
Pioneer of the American method of facial reconstruction, using ASTDs but not sculpting muscles

MIKHAIL MIKHAYLOVICH GERASIMOV
1907–70
Pioneer of the Russian method, using facial tissue depths from cadavers in the mortuary selected by resemblance, not population averages

RICHARD NEAVE
c. 1936–
Medical artist/facial reconstruction specialist who pioneered the Manchester 'combination method', reconstructing the full facial musculature

30-SECOND TEXT
Chris Rynn

The methods by which the full facial musculature can be reconstructed produce faces with distinctive features.

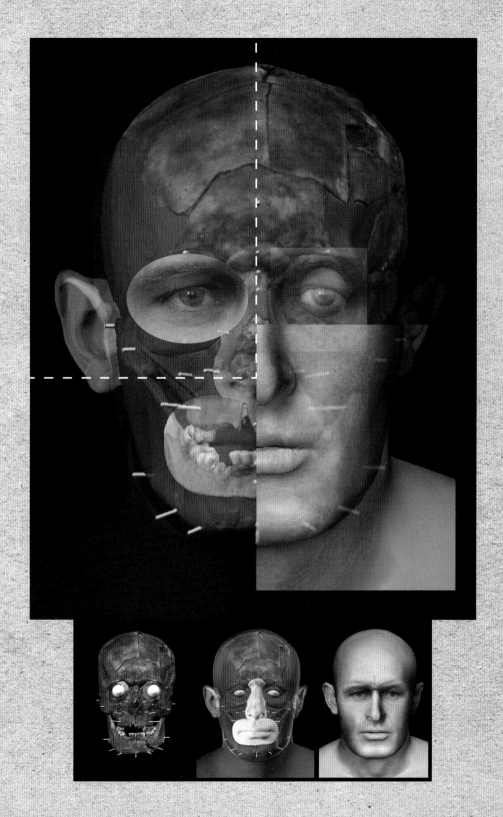

TIME DEATH INTERVAL

the 30-second scenario

3-SECOND CLUE
Establishing the time that has elapsed since death occurred is very important to the accurate analysis of a crime scene and the direction of its subsequent enquiry.

3-MINUTE EVIDENCE
Many changes occur in the bodies of mammals after death, all of which are associated with decomposition and putrefactive processes. Insects can be used to give a more accurate timeline, since species such as blowflies are attracted to dead bodies and will lay their eggs on exposed skin. These eggs and the hatched larvae remain on the body until they pupate. The larvae can be collected and their stage of development can be used to calculate the time elapsed since death.

Unless the death of an individual is witnessed, the time that has elapsed since death must be calculated using information from the body itself – and knowing exactly when a victim died may be of vital importance to an investigation. Immediately after death, changes occur within the body as cells break down and decomposition and putrefaction commence. These changes include algor mortis, or body cooling; livor mortis, in which the red blood cells sink under the influence of gravity; and rigor mortis, the stiffening of the muscles. As these changes happen reasonably sequentially, and have been described by researchers, an observation of them will allow a calculation of the time since death. However, other internal and external factors can influence the accuracy of this estimation. Other changes that are linked to the decomposition process, such as the breakdown of soft tissue, are affected by many biotic factors (living components that impact on the body, including bacteria, insects, scavengers and other humans) and abiotic factors (non-living parts of the environment including weather, soil and temperature) resulting in estimates of a time death interval rather than certainty.

RELATED TOPIC
See also
FORENSIC ENTOMOLOGY
page 102

3-SECOND BIOGRAPHY
WILLIAM BASS
1928–
One of the founders of a research area at the University of Tennessee in Knoxville, USA, where human decomposition is studied using cadavers. This was the first facility of its kind and continues to be the most well known. Bass established it when he realized how little was known about what happens to the body after death

30-SECOND TEXT
Lucina Hackman

Decomposition is a time-related process and is highly dependent on ambient temperature and other external environmental factors.

TRAUMA

the 30-second scenario

Trauma is generally caused by external force inflicted on either the soft or hard tissues of the body, or both at the same time. Trauma is described by its location on the body, its appearance and the type of force that has caused it. When referring to trauma, the time that it was inflicted is also included in this description; if the injury occurred before death it is referred to as being antemortem, at or around the time of death as perimortem, and occurring after death as post-mortem. There are four main types of soft tissue injuries: abrasions, bruises (also known as contusions), lacerations and incised wounds, and these may be caused by sharp, blunt or fragmenting forces. Each will cause different patterns of trauma and most damage occurs to the soft tissue, which may not always result in underlying bone damage. Trauma can be used to gain an understanding of both the manner and cause of death allowing the events leading up to the time of death to be recreated. Additionally, tools may leave marks that can lead to their identification, including shoe prints or knife wounds. When soft tissue is absent, damage to bones caused by blunt, sharp or ballistic trauma can still help to recreate past events.

3-SECOND CLUE
Trauma is the term used to describe damage inflicted upon soft (skin, muscles and so forth) and the hard tissues (bones, teeth) of the body by an external force.

3-MINUTE EVIDENCE
Bones most commonly respond to trauma by fracturing. The simplest fracture is linear and the most complex is comminuted, where the bone is broken into many fragments. Specific fracture patterns occur whether the bone is broken by blunt force trauma, sharp force trauma or ballistic trauma. When fracturing either heals naturally or through surgical intervention, the resulting appearance is always altered, therefore leaving tell-tale signs that previous trauma has occurred.

RELATED TOPICS
See also
DISMEMBERMENT
page 30

TOOL MARK ANALYSIS
page 76

3-SECOND BIOGRAPHIES
ANTISTIUS
died c. 10 or 11 CE
Roman physician who performed the autopsy on the body of Julius Caesar in 44 BCE. He identified 23 stab wounds of which only one was fatal. The post-mortem report is said to be the first recorded episode of the use of medical expertise in a murder investigation

KEITH SIMPSON
1907–85
English forensic pathologist, a founder member and President of the Association of Forensic Medicine. He wrote a standard text in forensic pathology, which described and identified the effects of trauma on the body, and which is still in print today

30-SECOND TEXT
Lucina Hackman

Wounds inflicted on the body can inform regarding the manner and the cause of death.

DISMEMBERMENT

the 30-second scenario

3-SECOND CLUE
While murder might be the most heinous crime perpetrated on a fellow human being, the desecration of the body by dismemberment is legally viewed as an aggravated homicide.

3-MINUTE EVIDENCE
Dismemberment of a body is most frequently undertaken by commonly available domestic knives and saws. However, other more exotic tools have been recorded including chainsaws, guillotines, boat propellers, swords and wood chippers. It is most common for a body to be cut into six parts – head, torso, two upper and two lower limbs – and for the parts to be wrapped in plastic before being deposited in water, such as a river, canal or lake.

The criminal dismemberment of a body usually occurs following murder or manslaughter, most commonly in the dwelling house of either the victim or the perpetrator, the perpetrator is usually known to the victim, drugs and/or alcohol are frequently involved and it is rarely premeditated or serial in nature. Researchers have identified five classifications of dismemberment: defensive dismemberment is the most common form and arises as a direct result of an attempt to conceal the crime, dispose of the remains or conceal the identity of the deceased; aggressive dismemberment is a continuation of the same aggressive emotions that cause the killing in the first place and may be referred to as 'overkill'; offensive dismemberment often confirms a sexual gratification or sadistic pleasure in the act of cutting; necromanic dismemberment refers to retaining body parts as trophies or fetishes; and communication dismemberment is used as a means of sending a message of warning to others. It is possible to learn much from examination of dismembered remains since, on most occasions, the actions of the perpetrators will result in cuts through bones. Information can be gleaned about the type of implement used, the position of the body during cutting and the order of the cuts.

RELATED TOPICS
See also
FORENSIC ANTHROPOLOGY
page 16

SIR BERNARD SPILSBURY
page 20

TOOL MARK ANALYSIS
page 76

3-SECOND BIOGRAPHIES
BILL HAGLUND
1943–
Forensic anthropologist, a prolific author and the senior forensic adviser for the International Criminal Tribunal for the conflicts in Rwanda and also for the former Yugoslavia. In both, dismemberment was a common trauma that was witnessed

HELINÄ HÄKKÄNEN-NYHOLM
1971–
Finnish psychologist who has studied and written about the psychology of dismemberment. She is also a forensic criminal profiler, and an adviser to the Finnish police

30-SECOND TEXT
Lucina Hackman

Dismemberment may be for ritual or sadistic purposes, or as a means of disposal of a body.

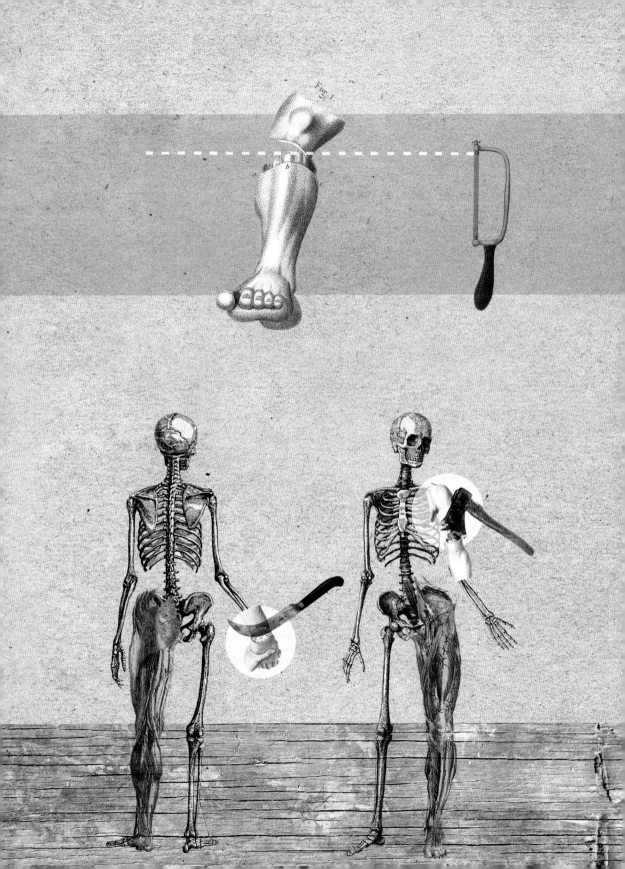

BIOMETRICS

BIOMETRICS
GLOSSARY

automated biometric An operator-free system for checking identity.

autonomic nervous system Part of the nervous system that is not under conscious control.

behavioural biometric A means of identifying a person through a behaviour, habit or an action, for example gait analysis, the way we walk.

buccal swab A sampling device used to collect a sample taken from inside a person's cheek for DNA testing.

copperplate, D'Nealian and **Spencerian** Specific and identifiable forms of handwriting with characteristic features.

copy genes Genetic material that is generated through gene duplication. A few duplicates, such as ribosomal RNA genes, remain active. *See also* pseudogenes.

fingerprint residues The secretions deposited when fingers come into contact with a surface.

genetic 'hotspots' Areas within the genome (*see below*) that show greater variation leading to genetic diversity.

genome The complete set of genetic material within a cell or an organism.

keloid scar A heaped-up scar that rises abruptly above the skin surface.

locus (plural **loci**) The specific place in the genome where a defined DNA sequence, such as a gene, is present.

ophthalmic surgeon A qualified physician who specializes in diseases of the eye and the orbit.

podiatry A clinical specialty that deals with the treatment and disorders of the foot and the ankle.

pseudogenes DNA sequences that are remnants of a gene duplication event and are now no longer active. *See also* copy genes.

short tandem repeats (STRs) Also known as microsatellites, short tandem repeats are DNA sequences of between 2 and 6 bases that are repeated one after the other (tandemly) but the number of times that these DNA sequences are repeated varies greatly, leading to high variation. As such, STRs are the standard means of DNA profiling.

split genes Almost all genes contain DNA sequences that encode a biomolecule interspersed with DNA sequences that are non-coding. The non-coding DNA sequences are called split genes.

DNA PROFILING

the 30-second scenario

The forensic test linking a sample from a crime scene to a person has been a powerful tool in forensic science since 1986. DNA profiling has revolutionized forensic biology and is now considered to be the gold standard of forensic practice. One of the benefits is that the same DNA profile is generated from blood, saliva, semen and skin cells; therefore, a buccal swab will generate a profile that can be compared with a blood sample or from a touched surface, for example, a knife handle or a drug wrap. The tests used are extremely sensitive, requiring fewer than 200 cells, which is typical residue from touching an item for a few seconds. It is assumed that every person's DNA is unique but it is not possible to test the entire genome and so several highly variable regions are selected. These are called short tandem repeats (STRs) and have been the bedrock of DNA profiling since 1994 when four STR regions (loci) were used. Over time, more loci have been added and now between 16 and 24 loci are tested – the more loci examined, the less chance of two persons sharing a profile, even if they are close relatives.

RELATED TOPICS
See also
SIR ALEC JEFFREYS
page 42

HAIR COMPARISON
page 58

BODY FLUIDS
page 66

BLOOD PATTERN ANALYSIS
page 82

3-SECOND BIOGRAPHY
PETER GILL
1952–
British forensic scientist
Involved at the start of DNA profiling, assisting with the very first case, and central to almost all the developments in DNA profiling, including the technology and interpretation of mixed DNA profiles

30-SECOND TEXT
Adrian Linacre

3-SECOND CLUE
DNA profiling is a forensic test to identify from whom biological material may have originated, utilizing variation in the genetic construction of the individual.

3-MINUTE EVIDENCE
Many countries have established a DNA database of persons found guilty of a crime; any sample collected, either from a person or at a scene, can be searched for or added to the database. The UK DNA database was established in 1995 and at the time of writing holds more than 6 million samples. There is a 45 per cent chance in the UK that a DNA profile from a crime scene will match with someone already stored on the database.

DNA from bodily fluids and skin cells can potentially link suspects to a crime scene or eliminate innocent individuals from enquiries.

FINGERPRINT ANALYSIS
the 30-second scenario

RELATED TOPIC
See also
DNA PROFILING
page 36

Almost all humans have fingerprints and mapping the loops, whorls and arches of their friction ridges has been used in criminal cases since the 1800s. These ridge patterns can be visualized using powders, chemicals or different light sources that detect natural oils, amino acids, proteins and other secretions present within residues that remain on a surface after touching. The print is photographed and the image compared directly to that of a known person or to millions of fingerprints stored in a database, creating a list of potential comparator prints. AFIS (Automated Fingerprint Identification System) is the most commonly used system. The final decision on a possible 'match' is made by an expert who will study a variety of features including the overall pattern and flow of the fingerprint, the number of ridges in specific areas and small details called minutiae. This comparison process is known as ACE-V: **A**ssessment of the quality of the fingerprint image; **C**omparison of the features in the recovered fingerprint with those in another fingerprint; **E**valuation of whether the fingerprints could be from the same person, excluded as coming from the same person or where no conclusion can be made; and **V**erification when another examiner analyses the results independently.

3-SECOND CLUE
Fingerprint analysis involves visualizing fingerprints deposited on various surfaces and comparing the features observed with those from a database or from a known individual.

3-MINUTE EVIDENCE
The quality of a fingerprint depends on the contact between the finger and the surface, whether the person is a good donor of residues and the freshness of the fingerprint. Some surfaces absorb different parts of the fingerprint residue and so the enhancement technique chosen is determined by the surface. There is also the chance that the prints cannot be identified: people who do rough manual work – for example, bricklayers – may lose their fingerprints through abrasion.

3-SECOND BIOGRAPHIES
FRANCIS GALTON
1822–1911
Half-cousin of Charles Darwin, Galton devised one of the first methods of classifying fingerprints, which is still in use in some parts of the world

WILLIAM JAMES HERSCHEL
1833–1917
British officer credited as the first person to suggest that fingerprints were unique to an individual and that fingerprints do not change substantively over someone's lifetime

HENRY FAULDS
1843–1930
Scottish physician who, in 1880, published in *Nature* the suggestion that fingerprints could be used for identification

30-SECOND TEXT
Niamh Nic Daéid & Sue Black

The suggested uniquenes. of fingerprints, hence thei value for identification purposes, was known in the nineteenth century.

Beginnings of Finger-printing — 1859 & 1860 — Selected originals, and Enlargements

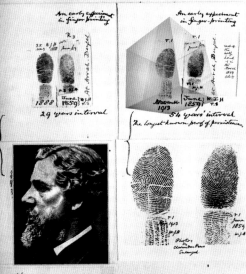

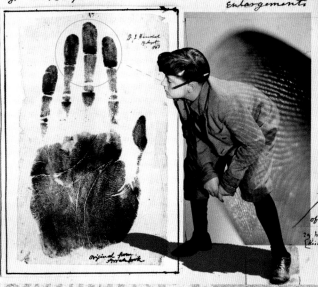

ANATOMICAL IDENTIFICATION

the 30-second scenario

3-SECOND CLUE
Every day of our lives we identify people we know through a visual analysis of their anatomy – the same can be true for forensic investigations.

3-MINUTE EVIDENCE
Anatomical or body modifications have a long human history. Approximately one in every three young adults has at least one tattoo and more than 1.5 million tattoos are drawn annually in the UK alone. More than 80 per cent of all adult females have at least one earlobe pierced, with the second most popular piercing being in the nostrils followed by the nipples. Oral piercings are most common in the tongue, and genital piercings are more common among women than men.

The human body is highly variable in its presentation and this variability may be used to compare individuals who are deceased with those who have been reported missing or to identify suspects and victims of crime. The skin offers many anatomical features of identity including its 36 different skin tones, which are not always uniform and can present as patches of freckles, birth marks, liver spots or moles. The location and pattern of these is random. The skin may be breached and have white or keloid scars or be altered permanently by dyes (tattoo), foreign objects (dermal implants) or piercings. The superficial pattern of veins under our skin can also be used to identify individuals and has been utilized as a reliable biometric to gain access to secure high-risk institutions because it is distinct to the individual. Additionally, the pattern of skin creases at the knuckles differs between all of our fingers and between each of our hands. The human body is not a mirror image of itself and the level of asymmetry within a person means that differences between people are of sufficient magnitude to be used for forensic identification purposes. This is true for identical twins who do not have identical anatomical features.

RELATED TOPICS
See also
AUTOPSY
page 14

FACIAL RECONSTRUCTION
page 24

FACIAL IMAGE COMPARISON
page 46

3-SECOND BIOGRAPHY
LADY RANDOLPH CHURCHILL
1854–1921
In nineteenth-century England, tattooing was a craze of the wealthy. Jennie Churchill was daring and was alleged to have the Talmudic symbol of eternity (a snake holding its tail in its mouth) tattooed on her wrist. There is no photographic proof of this though and it was said that she hid it from public view with long sleeves and bracelets

30-SECOND TEXT
Sue Black

Anatomical identification relies on recognizing visual differences ranging from distinguishing marks such as moles and scars to body art.

1950
Born in Oxford, England

1972
Graduates with a BA
in Biochemistry from
Merton College, Oxford

1975
Completes PhD on
mitochondria of cultured
mammalian cells at
University of Oxford

1984
Research shows that DNA
varies between individuals

1985
Provides evidence in
immigration case

1986
Elected a Fellow of the
Royal Society

1988
R v Colin Pitchfork – first
person to be convicted
through DNA evidence

1992
Made a Freeman of the
City of Leicester

1994
Knighted for services
to genetics

1996
Wins the Albert Einstein
World Award of Science

2004
Awarded the Royal Medal
of the Royal Society

2014
Awarded the Copley Medal
of the Royal Society

2017
Awarded the Companion
of Honour

When he was eight years old,

Alec Jeffreys was given a chemistry set by his father, which he used to create explosions and bad smells. By age 12 he was exploring the natural world through the dissection of bumblebees and dead cats. He later won a scholarship to study at Merton College, Oxford, and in 1972 he graduated with a BA in Biochemistry and then in 1975 with a PhD. By now he had moved into the world of medical genetics.

His eureka moment came when he was working on a DNA experiment in 1984 as he tried to understand why there were differences in the DNA samples of members of his technician's family. The realization was that DNA is not identical and from that came the possibility that individuals might be identifiable from their DNA.

Jeffreys has advised on several high-profile legal cases but the first was in 1985 when he helped to resolve a disputed immigration case relating to a Ghanaian child. The familial relationships were complex, but he showed that the father's DNA profile could be constructed from those of his known children, and the child was confirmed as belonging to the family thereby satisfying the Home Office and allowing entry into the UK.

In 1988 Jeffreys gave evidence in the first ever case in which DNA was used to identify a murderer. Colin Pitchfork was found guilty of the rape and murder of 15-year-old Lynda Mann in Leicestershire, England. Pitchfork then admitted to more than 1,000 incidents of indecent exposure as well as Lynda's murder and was given a minimum sentence of 30 years, which was reduced to 28 on appeal.

Although Jeffreys' great global breakthrough was in forensic science, his personal passion remained in medical genetics, developing new and powerful techniques to detect spontaneous change in genetic information as it transfers from parent to child. These so-called 'hotspots' are something of a paradox. They cause recombination, which in turn drives genetic diversity and evolution, but ironically the process also strongly favours mutations that suppress recombination. These mutations may stop a hotspot from working, which will ultimately deter recombination, and so, as Jeffreys reflected, 'hotspots contain within them the seeds of their own destruction'. Jeffreys was also the first to discover copy genes, split genes and pseudogenes.

Jeffreys has received many awards, medals and honorary degrees and was knighted by Her Majesty the Queen for his services to genetics in 1994 and then elevated to a Companion of Honour in 2017. He claims that to relax he likes to surf in Cornwall and to read 'unimproving' novels.

Sue Black

GAIT ANALYSIS

the 30-second scenario

Forensic gait analysis involves the matching of two sets of video images to compare the manner of walking of the person(s) of interest. One set of images is usually recovered from closed circuit television (CCTV) cameras near to the scene of a crime and the other is usually that of a suspect in police custody. Gait analysis includes not only study of the motion of the lower limbs but also the dynamics of the whole body as walking involves concomitant movement of the trunk, upper limbs, head and neck. Gait is a cyclical action and each cycle is referred to as a stride. Each is comprised of a stance and a swing phase. Stance is that part of the cycle that begins with the heel strike when the foot first meets the ground. This passes into a support phase when weight is transferred across the foot and terminates with the toe-off, which then initiates the swing phase of the other foot. Practitioners may also examine the footprint either on a surface such as soft, damp earth, or the wear pattern it leaves within a shoe. Forensic gait analysis is in its infancy and still requires considerable research before there is confidence in its use in the courtroom.

3-SECOND CLUE
There is no doubt that we can identify, from a considerable distance, someone we know by recognizing the way they walk and carry themselves.

3-MINUTE EVIDENCE
Between 2007 and 2016 13 dismembered feet encased only in socks and shoes, were washed ashore in British Columbia, Canada. The feet had separated from their respective bodies because of marine decomposition and the footwear had helped to retain the feet intact. Subsequently many of the individuals were identified as accidental drownings and it is thought that advances in shoe technology resulted in a lighter-weight shoe that could float and therefore be washed inshore more easily – a pedal flotation device.

RELATED TOPICS
See also
AUTOPSY
page 14

FORENSIC ANTHROPOLOGY
page 16

DISMEMBERMENT
page 30

3-SECOND BIOGRAPHY
NORMAN GUNN
1924–2015
A Canadian air force veteran of the Second World War, who was also a podiatric physician. Dr Gunn was the first podiatrist to undertake forensic casework in the 1970s and is regarded as the founder of the discipline

30-SECOND TEXT
Sue Black

Assessing human motion can potentially identify any biomechanical abnormalities in the way an individual walks or runs – a useful tool when comparing images caught on camera with potential suspects.

FACIAL IMAGE COMPARISON

the 30-second scenario

3-SECOND CLUE
Forensic facial image comparison involves the analysis of CCTV footage, crimes caught-on-camera by witnesses and suspect 'mug shots' taken by the police.

3-MINUTE EVIDENCE
CCTV is unusually prevalent in the UK, which has less than 5 per cent of the world's population, monitored by about a fifth of the world's CCTV cameras. Mounted high above the street CCTV is very useful for tracking suspects who are moving across a wide area, but less so for forensic identification from facial image comparison. Privately owned CCTV, inside shops for instance, is much higher quality and much lower down, closer to head-height and closer to the face, producing imagery more suitable for facial image comparison to the 'mug shots' of a suspect.

The face is a complex, asymmetrical three-dimensional shape where changes of expression alter its appearance markedly. Forensic facial image comparison is not a matching process like DNA or fingerprint comparison. It is, in fact, nearly impossible to superimpose two photographs of the same face precisely, even with the same camera and under controlled conditions. It is almost impossible, therefore, for facial comparison to provide conclusive proof of identity but it is possible to exclude definitively a suspect from being the offender, perhaps because of the shape of the face, position of the hairline or individual facial features that cannot be explained by differences in camera angle, lighting or anything image-related. Forensic imagery tends to originate either from a significant distance at a great height (CCTV) or from a smartphone, close enough to cause lens distortion. There is a six-level scale of support, phrased specifically to reflect these limitations in comparing facial images. 0) 'No support' denotes exclusion: the suspect and offender are demonstrably different individuals. The scale proceeds as follows: 1) Limited support; 2) Moderate support; 3) Support; 4) Strong support; and 5) Powerful support. Notably, there is no definitive positive identification beyond 'Powerful support' that the suspect and offender are one and the same individual.

RELATED TOPICS
See also
FACIAL RECONSTRUCTION
page 24

ANATOMICAL IDENTIFICATION
page 40

VIDEO ANALYSIS
page 120

DIGITAL DEVICES
page 128

3-SECOND BIOGRAPHY
FACIAL IDENTIFICATION SCIENTIFIC WORKING GROUP
est. 1997
Organization established to develop consensus standards, guidelines and best practices for the discipline of image-based comparisons of human features

30-SECOND TEXT
Chris Rynn

Accurately matching a face to a photograph, video recording or a victim's recollection is hampered by the ease with which individuals can alter or disguise their features.

CRIME CLASS

∂ 6   B788

Height,	1 m 76.1	Head, Lgth,	18.6	L. Foot.	27.4		Circle,		Age		Year
Eng. Hght.		" Width,	14.3	L. Mid. F.	12.6		Periph. Z.		Weight		
Outs, A,	1 m	Cheek,		L. Lit. F.			Pecul.		Build		
Trunk,		Right Ear { Lgth,		L. Fore A.	49.9				Comp.		
Carv.,		Width									

REMARKS RELATIVE TO MEASUREMENTS:

▷▷   4293   ▷▷   4243

DESCRIPTIVE.

Forehead.	Incl.	Nose.	Profile { Ridge		Right Ear	Border,	Hair	
	Hght.		Profile { Base	Root		Lobe,	Style Beard	
	Width.		DIMENSIONS.				Colour Beard	
	Pecul.		Length	Projection	Breadth	Teeth,		
			Pecul.			Chin,		

MEASURED AT ....

DATE ....   **BY** ....

IRIS RECOGNITION

the 30-second scenario

3-SECOND CLUE
Iris pattern recognition is an automated biometric that compares the complex pattern of the minutiae of the iris of the eye for identification purposes.

3-MINUTE EVIDENCE
In 2011, the Indian Aadhaar biometric project was launched. A unique 12-digit code was issued to each enrolee based on their biometric identity and this included iris scanning. By 2017 over 1.2 billion citizens were enrolled, making this the largest state biometric programme ever attempted. The cost is anticipated to be more than $1.3 billion so far and has generated great concern over privacy, fraud and the ability to maintain the ambitious programme.

The variation represented in the iris of the eye was first recognized by ophthalmic surgeons who believed its potential to far exceed that of fingerprinting for identification purposes. Iris recognition systems capture images in the near infrared wavelength, which permit visualization of the chromophore or melanin pigmentation of the iris. The iris is strongly pigmented through a mixture of two types of melanin – eumelanin and pheomelanin. Its purpose is to regulate the amount of light that enters the eye through the pupil and therefore it is controlled by the autonomic nervous system. The iris is a meshwork of connective tissue that displays arching ligaments, ridges, crypts, contraction furrows, a corona and a pupillary frill. Like fingerprints, the meshwork of the iris provides minutiae that are highly variable. The iris texture is said to be random or even chaotic. Mathematical algorithms and specific transformations allow iris scans to be matched for the purposes of identification or verification. Being an integral part of the body, iris pattern recognition is considered a secure biometric but research has shown that systems can be fooled easily (spoofed) with low-tech ease and this will only be overcome if we are able to incorporate live-tissue verification.

RELATED TOPICS
See also
FINGERPRINT ANALYSIS
page 38

ANATOMICAL IDENTIFICATION
page 40

GAIT ANALYSIS
page 44

3-SECOND BIOGRAPHY
JOHN DAUGMAN
1954–
British-American professor of computer vision and pattern recognition at the University of Cambridge, UK. He is the inventor of the IrisCode, one of the first algorithms for iris recognition biometric systems

30-SECOND TEXT
Sue Black

The complex and stable patterns of the iris can be used as an effective biometric for identification through the use of automatic scanning.

CLASSE **1** : Impigmentés

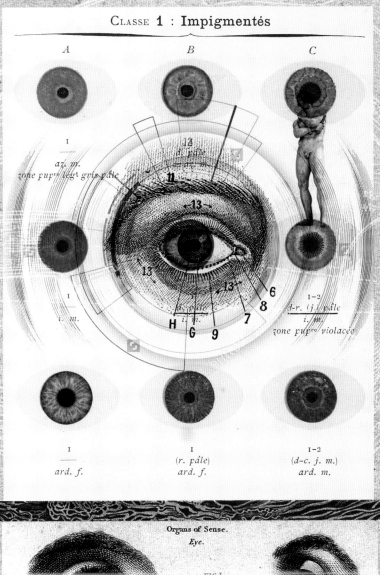

A	B	C
I	1½ d. jne	1-2
az. m.		d-r. (j.) pâle
zone pupre legt gris pâle		i. m.
		zone pupre violacée

I	I	1-2
ard. f.	(r. pâle)	(d-c. j. m.)
	ard. f.	ard. m.

Organs of Sense.
Eye.

FIG.I.

HANDWRITING ANALYSIS

the 30-second scenario

Learning to write usually starts at an early age and typically in a school environment. Different styles of handwriting (copperplate, Spencerian, D'Nealian, etc.) have been taught in different places at different times. It takes years of practice for the skill to develop and become sufficiently mature to produce adult handwriting. The different learning experiences and variable capabilities of people ensures that adults have handwriting that is unique to them, albeit that a person's handwriting varies from one time to another – known as natural variation. All handwritten elements may be examined including letters, numerals and other symbols. Signatures are a special case because they are not taught and do not have to comply with any conventions in their form and may be illegible. Relevant handwriting features observed (often with magnification) include the shape and structure of letters (some are rarer than others), the direction of pen movement (often an indicator of handedness) and the fluency (an indicator of skilled pen control). Handwriting may be changed deliberately, either to disguise it or when copying the handwriting of another person (especially where signatures are disputed) – these often lead to inferior handwriting. Handwriting deteriorates in the elderly or with certain pathological conditions such as Parkinson's disease.

RELATED TOPICS
See also
QUESTIONED DOCUMENT ANALYSIS
page 86

EXPERT WITNESS
page 138

ADMISSIBILITY
page 142

VALIDITY
page 140

3-SECOND CLUE
The purpose of forensic handwriting analysis (a sub-section of forensic document examination) is to determine the authorship of handwriting including signatures; it is not concerned with identifying a person's character.

3-MINUTE EVIDENCE
The confidence with which a handwriting analyst can confirm the identity of the writer is often predicated on the amount of text available to them, the distinctiveness of the script and the fluency of the writer. A famous case involving handwriting analysis was the kidnapping of Charles Lindbergh Jr in 1932. A letter demanding $50,000 ransom was found, although tragically the baby was killed. A comparison of the writing on the note and that of Bruno Hauptmann was positive and he was executed by electrocution.

3-SECOND BIOGRAPHIES
ALBERT S. OSBORN
1858–1946
American pioneer and author of an early textbook in the field, *Questioned Documents* (1910)

ORDWAY HILTON
1913–98
American statistician and author of *Scientific Examination of Questioned Documents* (1956), one of the most widely recognized texts in the field

30-SECOND TEXT
Mike Allen

Computers can be trained to assist in handwriting analysis but a human expert always takes the final decision.

Client Brief
Account Services
Creative Teams
Production Estimate
Production Estimate acceptance
Printing Costs
Mechanical Production
Always save as notepad
Save type as: All files
HTML
Head
Body
The artist's first coin punch

TRACES ◑

Acid Phosphatase (AP) testing A chemical test that detects acid phosphatase and indicates the presence of semen in a sample.

amylase An enzyme that helps to turn starch into sugar. Its detection is used as an indication of saliva in a sample.

aniline An organic compound used in the production of industrial chemicals

chemiluminescence Light that is produced as the result of a chemical reaction

DNA profiling The process used to obtain a DNA profile for the purpose of human identification in a forensic science context.

false positive Result that occurs when a test gives an indication of the presence of a particular target when it is not present.

haemoglobin The protein contained within red blood cells that carries oxygen.

Leuco Malachite Green (LMG) **test** A presumptive colour test used to indicate the presence of blood. The colour changes from colourless to blue/green if blood is present.

luminol A chemical that emits a blue glow when it interacts with blood and some other substances.

medulla The innermost part of a hair, and the part with most forensic value because it can be analysed for a DNA match.

microscopy The use of a microscope to visualize areas of materials that cannot be easily seen by the naked eye.

polarizing light microscope A microscope that uses a specialized form of light that can provide information about the structure of materials.

presumptive test A test that indicates that a particular target chemical may be present in a sample.

probative value Evidence that is deemed to be of value or importance in a trial.

quinine A medication that is used to treat malaria and other conditions.

refractive index A means of describing how light bends as it passes from one medium to another.

trace evidence Very small amounts of material, usually not visible to the naked eye, that can be transferred when objects/people make contact with each other.

volume crime A type of crime that is common or affects a lot of people, for example, car theft.

Scanning Electron Microscopy (SEM) A microscope that scans a material using a focused beam of electrons to produce an image.

GLASS

the 30-second scenario

Glass possesses some specific properties that dictate how it breaks. Modifications in its structure – for example, to strengthen it – can change how it breaks. When items made from glass, for example a window pane, are broken, fragments of glass can transfer to the clothing of the breaker, which can be recovered and analysed subsequently. Glass analysis normally involves measuring some of the physical and chemical properties of the material. The colour and curvature of the glass will be determined – whether it is flat from a window, or curved from a container or bottle. The main comparative analysis of glass is by measuring its refractive index and comparing this to glass taken from the crime scene or other known source. The refractive index values for different types of glass (domestic window, car window, windscreen, container) all have ranges of values, some of which overlap. Elemental analysis of the glass is also sometimes undertaken but again values overlap across different glass types. This means that while it may be possible to determine the type of glass from which a fragment originated, it is not possible to determine the specific source of the glass with certainty unless it can be pieced back together, a little like a jigsaw puzzle.

RELATED TOPIC
See also
EVIDENCE INTERPRETATION
page 148

3-SECOND CLUE
Glass is a material that is ubiquitous to modern society and it is frequently encountered as an evidence type across all forms of criminal activity, but most commonly in volume crime.

3-MINUTE EVIDENCE
Glass analysis is encountered frequently as evidence in a trial but its probative value can be low. Some literature suggests that about one in 12 people have glass on their clothing or footwear as a consequence of day-to-day living and it is not unusual to find glass from more than one source on clothing. The value that glass evidence brings to a criminal case is one offering a potential association and/or corroboration of events rather than something more absolute.

3-SECOND BIOGRAPHIES
JABIR IBN HAYYAN
c. 721–c. 815
Persian alchemist, chemist and polymath who described 46 recipes for producing coloured glass in his book *Kitab al-Durra al-Maknuna*

IRVING WIGHTMAN COLBURN
1861–1917
American inventor who developed a method for the production of flat glass sheets, which led to the mass production of window panes

30-SECOND TEXT
Niamh Nic Daéid

Fragments of glass that may cling to clothing, hair or footwear can be characterized by forensic glass analysis to indicate potential links to a crime scene or road accident.

HAIR COMPARISON

the 30-second scenario

Hairs are routinely found at crime scenes as humans naturally lose approximately 100 hairs a day. The first step is to ascertain whether a hair is human, and then determine from what part of the body it originated. Human scalp hair is more commonly encountered than, for example, pubic hair, which can be associated with sexual assaults, and these two hair types can be differentiated by microscopic features. Hairs have a simple three-layer structure, common to all mammals. The outer cellular layer, or cuticle, is normally composed of a single layer of cells that surrounds the pigmented cortex, which in turn surrounds the medulla, the innermost layer of the hair shaft. A hair from a human scalp can be differentiated from other mammals based on the cuticle pattern. In addition, human scalp hairs have a constant diameter and do not taper, do not exhibit banding and have a medulla that is greater than one-third of the total diameter of the hair. Comparison of hairs has not only been used to differentiate human from animal hair, but also to associate a suspect with a crime scene. This requires a representative collection from the individual because hairs can vary microscopically across the scalp, for example, the hairs on the temple can be much finer than those on the crown.

RELATED TOPICS
See also
DNA PROFILING
page 36

STABLE ISOTOPE ANALYSIS
page 114

3-SECOND CLUE
Hair comparison requires collection of representative hair samples from an individual for comparison, either through microscopy or by DNA profiling, with samples collected during a forensic investigation.

3-MINUTE EVIDENCE
Hairs can be transferred readily between persons, for example a victim and assailant, during a fight or a sexual assault. Microscopy is a simple, non-destructive test that can exclude the hairs as being from a person (such as a suspect) meaning that no further tests are required. If the suspect has similar hair (colour, length and microscopic type) then the next step will be to generate a DNA profile from the hair root because DNA profiling will give far greater confidence in any association.

3-SECOND BIOGRAPHY
PAUL KIRK
1902–70
American chemist who wrote *Human Hair Studies* in 1940. He specialized in microscopy and is attributed with defining forensic science as an 'identification' and an 'individualization' process

30-SECOND TEXT
Adrian Linacre

A single strand of hair can yield valuable information for forensic investigations. Length, colour and curliness are characteristics revealed macroscopically; DNA analysis of the medulla can identify a match.

FIBRES

the 30-second scenario

Textile fibres can be natural or man-made materials, or somewhere in between. Fibres are transferred easily from surface to surface depending on the nature of the fibre, the type of receiving surface (for example, another fabric) and the nature of the activity (sitting, fighting, and so on). Forensic examination of fibres starts with the recovery of the fibre from a surface, normally undertaken by using sticky tape to 'tape lift' the surface so that any loose fibres stick to the tape. The fibres of interest are then removed from the tape and examined using a polarizing light microscope, which enables a scientist to determine the type of fibre (say, cotton, nylon or polyester). Reference fibres taken from a known source such as the clothing of a victim can then be compared with the recovered fibres to determine whether they are of the same type. If a fibre is dyed then the dye can be extracted with solvents and compared with dyes extracted from the reference sample. Because garments and textiles are mass produced, the interpretation of similarities between fibres recovered from a suspect with reference samples must be made with caution. Databases can be used that indicate how common various fibres may be; changes in fashion and seasonal wear are also things that need to be factored into the interpretation of the weight placed on the evidence.

RELATED TOPICS

See also
DYES & PIGMENTS
page 70

EVIDENCE INTERPRETATION
page 148

3-SECOND BIOGRAPHY
MIKE GRIEVE
1942–2002
English forensic expert who set up the fibre section of the UK Metropolitan Police Forensic Science Laboratory in the 1960s and then the European Fibre Group in 2003. One of the foremost researchers in forensic fibre examination for many years

30-SECOND TEXT
Niamh Nic Daéid

3-SECOND CLUE
Textile fibres are one of the most common materials found as a consequence of a crime and appear frequently as forensic evidence in a wide variety of cases.

3-MINUTE EVIDENCE
Fibre evidence is considered an important corroborating evidence and can be used to provide associations or exclusions between people and places. Fibre evidence played an important part in a variety of high-profile murder cases in the UK including the murder of Sarah Payne in 2001, the murders of Jessica Chapman and Holly Wells in 2003 and the murder of six women (Gemma Adams, Tania Nicol, Anneli Alderton, Paula Clennell and Annette Nicholls) in Suffolk in 2008.

Fibres, along with hair, are often presented as evidence when trying to establish an association between a suspect and a victim or a crime scene.

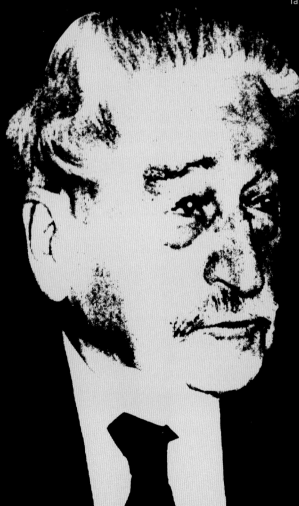

1877
Born in Saint-Chamond,
France

1902
Qualifies in Medicine in
Lyon, France

1907
Qualifies in Law and is
called to the Bar

1908
Travels to Paris to study
with French criminologist
Alphonse Bertillon

1910
Founds criminal
laboratory in Lyon

1912
His laboratory is officially
recognized by Lyon
Police, making it the
first police crime
laboratory in the world

1929
Forms the International
Academy of Criminalistics
in Lausanne, Switzerland

1931–35
Publishes the seven-
volume *Traité de
Criminalistique*

1966
Dies in Lyon aged 88

2012
Nominated into the
French Forensic Hall
of Fame of the
Association Québécoise
de Criminalıstıque

EDMOND LOCARD

Edmond Locard is viewed as one of the founding fathers of forensic science. He was a polymath, having strong foundations in science, medicine, arts and law, and greatly encouraged a scientific approach to the examination of items of potential evidence gathered from crime scenes. Such an approach was at the forefront of his mind when he convinced the French police to establish a laboratory in the attic of the courthouse in Lyon to collect and examine items recovered from crime scenes. Two years later in 1912, the laboratory was officially recognized as the world's first police scientific laboratory, gaining global recognition and admiration. Locard is also well regarded for advancing the study of fingerprints with a specific focus on the study of impressions of fingerprint pores. Through his writings and practice, Locard developed the examination, comparison and interpretation of fingerprint evidence beyond simple comparison of the superficial details by incorporating the minutiae of the ridge detail of the marks and prints.

Probably his biggest contribution to forensic science is through the principles he developed for explaining one of the underpinning philosophies of the evaluation and interpretation of forensic evidence. Locard proposed an overarching principle stating that, 'any action of an individual, and obviously the violent action constituting a crime, cannot occur without leaving a trace.' This has been shortened to 'every contact leaves a trace' and has become known as Locard's exchange principle. Simply put, this suggests that when two items come into contact with each other a transfer of material takes place. This transfer can be one way, from one object to the other, or two way, when both objects transfer materials to each other. Locard's exchange principle has become the cornerstone of criminalistics and solidified the importance of trace evidence recovered from crime scenes, victims and accused persons. In current forensic science practice, the interpretation and evaluation of recovered trace evidence within the context and framework of a specific set of circumstances or alleged activity have taken a central position in the role of the expert. We still lack the transfer, persistence and recovery studies across many evidence types to be in a position to fully evaluate Locard's exchange principle. His legacy to us has been to identify the importance of understanding and scientifically validating how the simple observation that 'every contact leaves a trace' can become truly explorative and meaningful in resolving criminal cases.

Niamh Nic Daéid

PAINT

the 30-second scenario

Paint is a very common material found in domestic and commercial properties and on vehicles. The types of paint used in buildings and that used on vehicles is different but in each case usually multiple layers of paint are present. Paint is made up of a range of components, each of which provides a specific function. These include pigments to impart colour, binders to hold the components together, solvents that act to carry the pigments and binders, and finally other additives to provide specific qualities, such as making the paint easier to spread. When paint is encountered in forensic science it is normally as multilayered fragments or flakes recovered from clothing, the surface of a vehicle or a tool (such as a screwdriver). Once a paint flake is recovered it will be examined under a microscope to identify how many layers are present. This will be compared with known paint recovered from a crime scene or scene of a collision. If the layers appear the same in terms of width, colour and sequence, further investigation into the chemical composition of the paint layers will normally be carried out. Each layer of paint is of itself a separate paint mixture and is examined chemically, first using a microscope and then an instrument that determines the chemical composition.

3-SECOND CLUE
Paint is a common form of trace evidence often recovered from incidents involving road traffic accidents or breaking and entering.

3-MINUTE EVIDENCE
When paint evidence is presented in court the expert describes the type of paint and number of layers. Paint can transfer when a painted surface is disrupted, for example in a collision between two vehicles, or where paint is scraped off, such as when a tool is used to force open a painted window. Two-way transfer of paint between both painted surfaces when they come together can provide strong evidence of an interaction between the surfaces.

RELATED TOPICS
See also
DYES & PIGMENTS
page 70

EVIDENCE INTERPRETATION
page 148

3-SECOND BIOGRAPHY
ALBERT HENRY MUNSELL
1858–1918
American painter and teacher of art who invented the Munsell colour system, still used today to numerically code and describe colour in materials

30-SECOND TEXT
Niamh Nic Daéid

Following a collision, paint analysis experts may be able to narrow down a vehicle's make, model, even its year of manufacture from paint chips recovered from the scene of an accident or a crime.

BODY FLUIDS

the 30-second scenario

The three principal body fluids

are blood, semen and saliva. Without knowing which body fluid is present, any resulting DNA profile has little context and may be non-informative, but it will have provided a possible link to the potential donor. The body fluid is subjected to a range of presumptive tests. For blood, this relies on a colour reaction that occurs when haemoglobin is present. The Leuco Malachite Green (LMG) test reacts with the haem group in red blood cells, giving a colour change from colourless to light blue. The chemical luminol is also used to test for blood and results in a chemiluminescence (a light) if blood is present. Although highly sensitive, this test needs to be performed in virtual darkness. False positives occur in the presence of other chemicals, such as plant peroxides, and therefore caution is advocated when reporting results. Semen stains can be identified using Acid Phosphatase (AP) testing, which gives a rapid positive result if semen is present. The presence of amylase is used to indicate saliva. Amylase is only present in a few other body fluids, such as pancreatic fluids, but unlike the test for blood or semen, it takes at least 30 minutes to complete.

3-SECOND CLUE
When a body fluid is encountered in forensic investigation, the initial step is to perform one of a range of presumptive tests and then pass the sample on for DNA profiling.

3-MINUTE EVIDENCE
DNA profiling is an excellent way to determine from whom cells have originated, but unless the source, that is, the body fluid, is known, its evidential power is reduced. By linking the body fluid to a person, it is further possible to comment on how and when the body fluid was transferred. The presumptive tests described here can also be used to analyse mixtures of body fluids, such as blood and semen.

RELATED TOPICS
See also
DNA PROFILING
page 36

BLOOD PATTERN ANALYSIS
page 82

3-SECOND BIOGRAPHY
KARL LANDSTEINER
1868–1943
Austrian biologist, physician and immunologist who distinguished the main blood groups in 1901 (now termed ABO) and received a Nobel Prize in 1930

30-SECOND TEXT
Adrian Linacre

Investigators at crime scenes are able to use chemicals to detect residues of bodily fluid. One, luminol, has been used as early as 1939. Being highly sensitive it is capable of detecting quantities of blood as small as one part per million.

GUNSHOT RESIDUE
the 30-second scenario

3-SECOND CLUE
Gunshot Residue (GSR) is the expelled mixture of burnt and unburnt propellant, metallic fragments and primer components, produced when a firearm is discharged.

3-MINUTE EVIDENCE
To establish the presence and determine the individual characteristics of GSR, forensic specialists use Scanning Electron Microscopy to provide high-resolution magnification of particles that can be tens of microns (μm) in size and invisible to the naked eye. Due to the microscopic nature of GSR, this evidence type is very fragile and therefore has a relatively low persistence rate if subjected to physical disturbance, inclement climatic conditions and personal hygiene regimes such as washing.

Discharging a firearm requires the primer cap within the base end of a round of ammunition to be struck. Striking the primer begins a chain reaction, culminating in the expulsion of a projectile followed by hot gases, burnt and unburnt propellant, metallic fragments and trace amounts of primer mixture (ignition chemicals). This particulate matter is commonly referred to as Gunshot Residue (GSR). The dynamic pressures that are produced during a discharge not only propel the GSR forward along and out of the barrel, but also expel it out through any gap around the breech-face (the area that holds a round in the chamber) and barrel, potentially covering the firer and close surroundings in a cloud of fine particulates. During the forensic examination of a firearm discharge scene, investigators record and recover both visible and trace GSR samples to assist in determining distance from muzzle to target and, potentially, to enable comparison analysis with any recovered weapon, clothing or suspect. Typically, analysis of GSR is used in determining whether a suspect fired a weapon and is based around the trace components of the primer rather than the presence of burnt/unburnt propellants. In this form of GSR examination, the presence or absence of compounds used in the manufacture of the primer – Lead (Pb), Antimony (Sb) and Barium (Ba) – are what the forensic specialist will analyse.

RELATED TOPICS
See also
FIREARM ANALYSIS
& BALLISTICS
page 78

EXPLOSIVES
page 94

3-SECOND BIOGRAPHY
JEAN SAMUEL PAULY
1766–1821
Swiss gunsmith credited in 1808, along with François Prélat, with designing and patenting the first self-contained cartridge case featuring an integrated primer cap

30-SECOND TEXT
Grant Thomson

The act of firing a gun leaves multiple clues that corroborate or refute circumstances surrounding a firearm-related death, wounding or intent.

DYES & PIGMENTS

the 30-second scenario

Analysis of dyes and pigments is generally chemical and involves understanding both the organic and elemental composition of the dye or pigment. Dyes are mainly used in colouring fabrics although some are also used in inks. There is a wide range of sources for dyes which include plant materials such as berries, bark and leaves, as well as man-made dyes. Dyes are classified according to their chemical properties and their solubility. Pigments are solid materials that reflect and absorb different parts of visible light selectively. Pigments are insoluble in solvents, resulting in a suspension of the material. Like dyes, pigments can be synthetic or natural in origin: some – ochres and iron oxides, for example – have been used as colourants since prehistoric times. They are used to give colour to inks, cosmetics, fabrics and paint. Dyes form part of many presumptive tests for various materials of forensic significance including explosives, drugs and body fluids. Dyes are also components of a wide range of chemical enhancement techniques used for fingerprint analysis. The examination of dyes and pigments in a forensic science context involves extracting the dye or pigment from a questioned sample – lipstick on clothing, for instance – and comparing it to the extracted dye or pigment from a specific sample to provide evidence of a potential link.

3-SECOND CLUE
Dyes and pigments are both encountered in a range of forensic evidence types including ink, paint and fibres.

3-MINUTE EVIDENCE
Understanding the chemistry of different dyes and pigments has an important bearing on the analysis of a range of evidence types encountered in forensic science. This includes trace evidence (such as fibres and paint) as well as other evidence where colour is important such as inks, including writing and tattoo inks, and in some cases drugs and fuels where a dye or pigment may have been added.

RELATED TOPICS
See also
FIBRES
page 60

PAINT
page 64

QUESTIONED DOCUMENT
ANALYSIS
page 86

3-SECOND BIOGRAPHY
WILLIAM HENRY PERKIN
1838–1907
English chemist who discovered the first aniline dye at the age of 18 while trying to find synthesized quinine

30-SECOND TEXT
Niamh Nic Daéid

Analysis of pigments and dyes encountered in items presented as evidence can potentially provide inclusionary or exclusionary information.

PHYSICAL & CHEMICAL ANALYSIS

biotransformation Refers to the alteration of a substance in the body. Drug and toxin metabolism, whereby the drug or toxin molecule is changed to make the substance more water-soluble so that it can be excreted from the body in the urine or faeces, is an example of biotransformation. Most biotransformation takes place in the liver but it can also occur elsewhere in the body including in the gut and the kidneys.

chromatography Term used to describe a variety of means of separating different individual chemical molecules from a mixture of chemicals – drugs, for example, such as ecstasy or heroin (see page 90), based on their different properties. Once separated, the identity of individual chemical molecules can be determined using a simple colour reaction or machines known as detectors, which make use of a particular property of the molecule (for example, their mass, how they absorb light and energy, etc). The results from the colour test or detector for the separated molecules are then compared to a reference material whose identity is known and whose response to the chromatography and the detector is also known. The identity of the component parts can then be determined using a mass spectrometer (see opposite).

class characteristics Marks made by a particular type, or 'class' of implement, for example a saw, a knife or a screwdriver, as opposed to the marks made by a specific tool.

confirmatory test A test that proves the presence of a particular chemical compound in a sample or in a mixture of materials. Two different and independent confirmatory tests are often carried out to remove any doubt in the result, a procedure known as corroboration.

Exchange Principle The suggestion that every time there is contact between two people or between people and objects an exchange of physical materials occurs, attributed to Edmond Locard (see page 63).

exposure route The way that a drug gets into the body – toxins can be inhaled, injected, absorbed or ingested.

Firearm Discharge Residue (FDR) Another term for Gunshot Residue (see page 68).

Frye test Admissibility test for expert evidence used in some courts in the USA requiring a general acceptance of the reliability of a technique by the appropriate scientific community.

grazing light Also called an oblique light, this is a light that is shone at an angle onto a surface. It is commonly used to photograph impressions, fingerprints and tool marks.

gyroscopic spin The spin imparted on a projectile as it is fired out of a rifled barrel.

homemade/improvised explosive devices (HED/IED) Explosive devices that are prepared using commercially available and/or common chemicals and other materials.

mass spectrometer A machine that is used to break chemical molecules into smaller pieces in characteristic patterns that allow the molecules to be identified.

modus operandi Latin expression that means a particular way of doing something. The term is often used to describe a criminal's methods.

new psychoactive substances (NPS)
A general name given to a range of synthetic chemical molecules produced to circumnavigate specific drug legislation. NPS have been previously called designer drugs, legal highs, bath salts and research chemicals. They are substances of abuse that are not controlled by international drug control laws but which may pose a public health threat. The term 'new' does not necessarily refer to newly created substances — some NPS were originally synthesized up to 40 years ago — but to substances that have recently emerged in the illegal drug market.

presumptive test A preliminary test that indicates in a substance the presence of certain chemical compounds or particular chemical bonds or atoms. Such tests are often highly sensitive (can detect tiny amounts of a substance) but may be non-specific (gives rise to false positives). In drugs testing, a presumptive test may indicate the family of drugs to which an unknown substance belongs, but not the exact drug. A confirmatory test (see opposite page) is then carried out.

smooth-bored and **rifled-barrel firearms**
Descriptions of different types of barrel used on weapons. A smooth-bore has no rifling, and a rifled barrel has a series of grooves on the inside of the barrel. *See also* gyroscopic spin.

TOOL MARK ANALYSIS

the 30-second scenario

A tool is a manual action or powered implement that has been designed to carry out a particular function. Whether designed for a specific purpose or improvised, tools are commonly used in the commission of crimes. Criminals may require them to facilitate opening a lockfast place, for example, cutting a padlock or forcing open a door. Much more rarely, the dismemberment of bodies can also involve the use of tools. When the harder tool comes into contact with the softer substrate, such as a window frame, impressed, striated and trace evidence from the tool can be imparted onto that substrate. Tool marks can be described as being created by pressure; lateral force and motion (dynamic); cutting; or multi-stroke, caused by a repetitive action. Analysis of the tool-mark evidence can determine the type and size of an implement (class characteristics), incidental manufacturing marks (subclass) and random imperfections including accidental damage (individual characteristics). Tool-mark evidence at a crime scene is recovered by taking the entire item, if possible; using 1:1 scaled macro photography to produce actual size images of the tool mark; and making casts of marks using silicone rubber-based materials. Test pieces made from suspect tools are then directly compared against recovered crime marks.

3-SECOND CLUE
Forensic tool mark analysis generally involves comparing characteristics produced by recovered suspect implements against marks recovered from a crime scene.

3-MINUTE EVIDENCE
Establishing the 'class' of tool(s) used in the commission of crimes, especially where a *modus operandi* has been linked, assists investigators with intelligence and negates the unnecessary submission of tools that do not match the criteria for examination against these particular crimes. For example, establishing a series of burglaries where a 5mm flat-bladed screwdriver with a square shank was used, negates the examination of same-sized round-shank screwdrivers.

RELATED TOPICS
See also
DISMEMBERMENT
page 30

EDMOND LOCARD
page 62

PAINT
page 64

FIREARM ANALYSIS
& BALLISTICS
page 78

3-SECOND BIOGRAPHY
HANS GROSS
1847–1915
Austrian law professor, judge and a pioneer of forensic science. He wrote *Handbuch für Unter-suchungsrichter als System der Kriminalistik* (1891), which referred to the recording and moulding of tool-mark impressions, along with the need for microscopic examinations of marks

30-SECOND TEXT
Grant Thomson

Tools, like weapons, bear class and individual characteristics that can leave their mark on surfaces with which they come into contact.

FIREARM ANALYSIS & BALLISTICS

the 30-second scenario

RELATED TOPICS
See also
GUNSHOT RESIDUE
page 68

TOOL MARK ANALYSIS
page 76

3-SECOND CLUE
The expert analysis of firearms involves comparing characteristics produced on fired cartridges and projectiles to ascertain weapon type and establish common origin between recovered evidence and suspect weapons.

3-MINUTE EVIDENCE
Generally, when a firearm's trigger is pulled, a firing pin pushes forwards striking the primer cap of the cartridge. A chemical reaction occurs when the primer is struck, which causes a rapid expansion of gases, which in turn forces the projectile from the cartridge casing and pushes it along and out of the barrel towards the target. This chemical reaction generates heat, smoke and particulate matter that is commonly referred to as Gun Shot Residue (GSR) or Firearm Discharge Residue (FDR).

A firearm, for example, a cannon, is a device that incorporates a tube from which projectiles propelled by kinetic energy are discharged towards an intended target. Modern firearms incorporate mechanical actions during loading, firing, extraction and/or ejection processes, along with magazine storage/feeding, that can impart characteristics onto cartridge cases and projectiles, such as bullets. Analysis of class characteristics aims to establish the make and model of the firearm while individual marks reflect imperfections in manufacture, wear and tear and, where applicable, indications of accidental damage. Firearms can either be smooth-bored or rifled-barrelled and small arms (handguns) or long arms (shoulder-fired weapons). Rifled-barrel weapons have a series of spiral grooves cut into the internal diameter of the barrel that create gyroscopic spin along the long axis of the fired projectile as it traverses the barrel. By examining rifling marks imparted onto the softer substrate of the projectile or bullet, firearm examiners can attempt to identify the calibre, make and model of the firearm used. Once a suspect weapon is recovered, test fires are conducted to compare any repeating marks and imperfections on cartridges or bullets to confirm whether there is sufficient agreement between them to indicate likely common origin.

3-SECOND BIOGRAPHIES
ALEXANDER J. FORSYTH
1768–1843
Scottish minister and game shooter who invented the percussion ignition system in 1807, using mercury fulminate, which was pivotal in the evolution of modern firearms

GERALD BURRARD
1888–1965
Author of several reference works on guns including *The Identification of Firearms and Forensic Ballistics* (1934) in which he advocated the use of microscopy and photography to satisfy juries of evidence of commonality between crime bullets and weapons

30-SECOND TEXT
Grant Thomson

Ballistic analysis is the study of the firearm, the projectile and the object with which it comes into contact.

FOOTWEAR MARKS

the 30-second scenario

The varied sizes and designs of soles allow footwear to be distinguished relatively easily. For example, most athletic soles are made of rubber or polymers, either cut from a larger layered piece or obtained by moulding, and can include multiple elements such as lines, zigzags, circles, etc. Additionally, worn soles acquire wear features and distinguishing defects (such as cuts). When shod individuals pass through crime scenes, their soles leave marks either as patent three-dimensional marks or as two-dimensional vestiges in dust or a contaminant (for example, blood). The latter can be detected with a grazing light or enhanced using chemical detection techniques. The locations of footwear marks can allow a forensic analyst to reconstruct actions that may have taken place, even to determine the number of individuals involved. If compared with other footwear marks, links between cases may be established. Marks can also be matched to reference collections to gain information on the brand, model or size of shoe or to identify potential suspects from footwear databases of arrested individuals. When a pair of shoes of a given person is seized, reference inked prints of the soles can be compared with marks collected from a crime scene. Side-by-side examination of the general and acquired features allows the expert to advise on whether the marks and prints share a likely common source. Evidence, so produced, can range from exclusions to extremely high degrees of association.

3-SECOND CLUE
Footwear marks left behind when we walk wearing shoes are signs of our presence, passage and activities.

3-MINUTE EVIDENCE
Even though shoes are mass produced, the ever evolving market, the multiple design of the soles, the number of moulds and minute variations mean that shoe soles can be distinguished from each other with a very high discrimination power. More than 95 per cent of sole designs and their associated marks can be told apart by visual inspection. The features of the shoe sole can be characterized using coding systems that help to identify the possible shoe types using databases of known manufactured shoes.

RELATED TOPICS
See also
GAIT ANALYSIS
page 44

TOOL MARK ANALYSIS
page 76

FORENSIC SOIL SCIENCE
page 112

3-SECOND BIOGRAPHY
WILLIAM J. BODZIAK
1946–
FBI expert in footwear and tyre impressions and author of *Forensic Footwear Evidence*. Bodziak has been a key expert witness in numerous high-profile cases such as the O. J. Simpson trial in 1995

30-SECOND TEXT
Christophe Champod

Soles of shoes that are designed to give traction on smooth or slippery surfaces can leave footwear marks at crime scenes which can possibly be linked to the shoes that left the marks.

BLOOD PATTERN ANALYSIS

the 30-second scenario

3-SECOND CLUE
Blood is the most commonly found body fluid encountered in forensic science, and is often used to create a DNA profile.

3-MINUTE EVIDENCE
Bloodstain pattern can be highly informative as a key reconstruction tool. Patterns are crucial, one spot does not make a pattern; but looking at a number of spots of blood and determining that they all come from a similar focal point allows the examiner to start to reconstruct the scene. Just by looking at the pattern of blood, an examiner can state whether an allegation of a violent assault is supported, compared to self-defence, for example.

Blood is shed in many violent assaults. Depending on the action creating the blood loss, a particular pattern may be created. For example, the pattern created from a gunshot wound would be very different to that from a stabbing or blood dripping from a wound. By looking at the stain pattern, it is therefore possible to differentiate between such actions. Interpretation of bloodstain patterns is a part of crime scene investigations, and conclusions are made in association with knowledge of the underpinning sciences (maths, physics and biology) to provide information on the physical events giving rise to the bloodstains and patterns observed. Bloodstain pattern analysis is therefore a reconstruction tool and provides information on the actions that may have occurred. When blood leaves the body, it travels as a ball and there is a simple relationship between the size of the ball and the force that created it – the higher the impact force then the smaller the spot. If the ball of blood lands on a surface at 90 degrees then a round stain is created, but as the angle becomes more acute the stain created becomes longer and thinner. Smaller balls of blood will travel less far, due to wind resistance and, therefore, combining the size and shape of a bloodstain can enable the analyst to make deductions as to the action that created the patterns.

RELATED TOPICS
See also
DNA PROFILING
page 36

BODY FLUIDS
page 66

3-SECOND BIOGRAPHY
PAUL L. KIRK
1902–70
American chemist and a founder of blood pattern analysis who gave an affidavit in the case of *State of Ohio v Samuel Sheppard* (1954). This was a significant case as blood pattern met the Frye Test and therefore was deemed admissible in many US states

30-SECOND TEXT
Adrian Linacre

High-resolution photography is a useful means of capturing evidence of violent assault. The shape, number and size of blood spatters may indicate the type of weapon used or the angle of impact.

1791
Born in Newington Butts (now London Borough of Southwark)

1813
Appointed as a Chemical Assistant at the Royal Institution

1821
Appointed Assistant Superintendent of the House of the Royal Institution, discovers electromagnetic rotations, the principle behind the electric motor. Marries Sarah Barnard

1824
Elected a fellow of the Royal Society and initiates the Royal Institution Christmas Lectures

1825
Appointed Director of the Laboratory of the Royal Institution, discovers benzene

1831
Discovers electromagnetic induction and invents the electromagnetic generator

1832
Receives honorary doctorate from Oxford University

1833
Appointed first Fullerian Professor of Chemistry

1835
Awarded a Civil List pension by the King

1845
Discovers diamagnetism

1846
Undertakes detailed investigation of coal dust explosions at Haswell where 95 miners died

1847
Discovers the optical properties of gold colloids – considered to be the foundational discovery for metallic nanoparticles

1859
Electrifies lighthouses for the first time

1862
Receives honorary doctorate from Cambridge University

1867
Dies at his Grace and Favour house at Hampton Court in London

MICHAEL FARADAY

As a child, Michael Faraday

received only a very basic schooling, becoming an apprentice bookbinder at age 14. During his apprenticeship he read many books, stimulating his interest in science. At the end of his apprenticeship he attended lectures presented by Humphry Davy at the Royal Institution and Royal Society, ultimately sending Davy a copy of his notes from those presentations. This established a lifelong relationship between the two men and spurred Davy to employ Faraday as a Chemical Assistant at the Royal Institution. Faraday joined Davy on a tour across Europe between 1813 and 1815, providing him with access to a wide network of scientific experts across the continent.

As his career progressed, Faraday was well recognized for his skills as a chemist, investigating the liquefaction of a variety of gases as well as working on steel alloys and developing a range of new types of glass with different optical properties. He also developed experimental tools to address the needs of his research as he went along. He is probably best known for his work on electricity, electrochemistry and electromagnetism developing many novel inventions within that domain.

Faraday was devoutly Christian and served as an Elder in the Sandemanian denomination, an offshoot of the Church of Scotland. He also used his skills and knowledge for public good undertaking 'forensic' investigations into industrial pollution and coal gas explosions where he appeared as an expert witness for the courts.

Faraday was passionate about education and was deeply engaged in bringing an understanding of science to the public. He established the Royal Institution Christmas Lecture series in 1825, which still runs today. In 1862 he appeared before the Public Schools Commission providing evidence about education in Great Britain. He was a gifted public lecturer, bringing fun and practical experimentation into the auditorium.

Faraday wrote a wide range of text books and letters about his work across his lifetime. He was honoured with many awards including the Royal Medal and Copley, Rumford and Albert medals. He was made a Fellow of a range of national scientific academies but refused presidency of the Royal Society on more than one occasion and turned down a knighthood. First and foremost, Michael Faraday was a scientific polymath, passionately curious about the world around him and equally passionate about experimentation, communication and having fun in demonstrating how science could be used to develop our understanding of the world.

Niamh Nic Daéid

QUESTIONED DOCUMENT ANALYSIS

the 30-second scenario

A questioned document is generally a paper document where there is a suggestion that either the content of the document has been altered or changed in some way, that the author of the document is unknown or that the document's authenticity is in question. By far the most common type of examination investigates alleged alterations or changes made in the text or in a signature. Here the properties of any ink present may be compared across the document using different lighting systems to see whether more than one type of ink has been used. Indentations on the document made because of writing, can also be checked to see if they match with the actual text present. The indentations on the sheet of paper which may have been beneath the questioned document is also examined in this way – for example, in a notebook the page beneath the page containing a suspected alteration would be examined. In cases involving anonymous writing, the questioned documents are examined physically to determine the type of ink used, or whether there are characteristic marks left from printers that may have been used to produce the document. The authentication of documents may include investigation of the paper type and the presence or absence of watermarks or other embedded features, or investigating the particular typeface or ink used on the document.

30-SECOND TEXT
Niamh Nic Daéid

Analysis of questioned documents can be used to provide circumstantial evidence of association between an individual and an altered text.

FIRE SCENE INVESTIGATION

the 30-second scenario

3-SECOND CLUE
Fire scene investigation involves the use of a wide range of skills across chemistry, physics and engineering to understand how fire events occur and develop.

3-MINUTE EVIDENCE
Fire investigation often involves teams of technical experts who will work together to understand where and how the fire started and how it spread. In some cases, because of the damage caused, it may not be possible to be definitive regarding the cause of a fire but a 'most likely' cause will be proffered. This can include overheating of materials due to chemical or biological reactions, the overheating of materials because of electrical faults, fire caused by lightning strikes or fire resulting from deliberate ignition (arson).

Fire scene investigators are trained to determine where and how a fire may have started. They often become involved in working out how the fire developed and use information and knowledge relating to how heat affects materials and how they burn. The development of fires inside buildings follows a well-defined sequence that leaves behind different patterns of damage (such as charring, discolouration or destruction) known as 'burn patterns' on surfaces and structures. These can be interpreted and used to try to recreate the most likely sequence of events. The first stage in a fire scene investigation is to gather background information relating to what transpired before the fire began. Next, a careful step-by-step investigation of the fire scene is undertaken where the burn patterns and damage observed are used to establish where the fire most likely started. This often involves removing layers of debris. Once the area of origin is known, the next step is to consider what may have caused the fire. The range of common causes include overheating and faults in electrical appliances, smouldering combustion or deliberate ignition. Fire scene investigators can also be involved in determining how fires spread in buildings. Their work is used in both criminal and civil cases, leading to recommendations about the way buildings, furnishings, appliances and vehicles are constructed and designed.

3-SECOND BIOGRAPHY
ROBERT BOYLE
1627–1691
Anglo-Irish chemist and one of the Royal Society's founders who worked on understanding the fundamental chemical nature of combustion

30-SECOND TEXT
Niamh Nic Daéid

The systematic removal of layers of debris that remain following a fire is known sometimes as 'digging out'. It allows investigators to carefully uncover physical evidence left after the fire.

DRUGS

the 30-second scenario

Drugs are substances that cause a chemical or biological (physiological) change in the user. Drugs taken as medicines can either be licensed for sale without restriction, for example, ibuprofen, or as prescription-only medicines. Some drugs are controlled under law as they are seen to be potentially harmful to the individual and to society and have a high risk of being misused. Such drugs are referred to as 'drugs of abuse'. Many controlled drugs have medical uses, for example the painkiller diamorphine, and diazepam, which is used to treat anxiety. Some controlled drugs have no medical uses and are made illegally, such as ecstasy (MDMA). Seized samples suspected of containing controlled substances, often powders, tablets or plant materials, are examined in a forensic drug-testing laboratory and their visual appearance is recorded. The sample undergoes a preliminary presumptive test, often a simple chemical reaction colour test, which provides information on the chemical family of the drugs present (diamorphine, for example, is an opiate). Based on these findings the drug undergoes further confirmatory testing using technique such as chromatography and mass spectrometry to identify the individual chemicals present in a way that satisfies the law. Many illegal drugs are mixtures of substances in powders or tablets at very variable concentrations and so can be highly unpredictable in their effects.

3-SECOND CLUE
A forensic drug chemist, tests unknown substances seized by organizations such as the police and customs department, to determine if controlled chemicals are present.

3-MINUTE EVIDENCE
In addition to 'traditional' drugs of abuse, such as cannabis, cocaine, amphetamines, ecstasy and heroin, a growing number of new drugs are appearing on the illegal market. These are often referred to as new psychoactive substances (NPS) and since 2008 more than 700 new drugs have been identified. They are less commonly used than the established drugs of abuse and many appear and disappear on the illegal drug market quite quickly.

RELATED TOPIC
See also
TOXICOLOGY
page 92

3-SECOND BIOGRAPHIES
FRIEDRICH SERTÜRNER
1783–1841
German pharmacist who was the first to isolate morphine from raw opium harvested from *Papaver somniferum*, the opium poppy, in 1817. He proved that morphine was the compound responsible for the effects of opium, which at that time was used as painkiller or sedative and often smoked as a drug of abuse

FRANCIS WILLIAM ASTON
1877–1945
British physicist and chemist who built the first mass spectrometer in 1919. It is now one of the most common scientific instruments in a modern forensic drugs laboratory and is used to identify controlled substances in seized samples

30-SECOND TEXT
Craig McKenzie

Cannabis, cocaine, amphetamines, ecstasy and heroin are the most commonly abused drugs in the world.

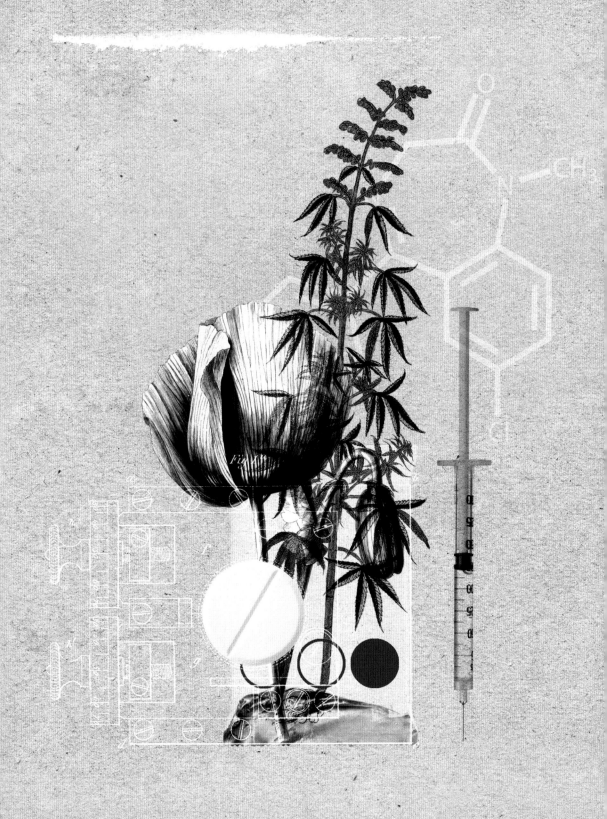

TOXICOLOGY

the 30-second scenario

3-SECOND CLUE
Forensic toxicology
involves the identification
of drugs and poisons in
biological samples such
as urine or blood, and
providing information
about the effects these
have in humans or, more
rarely, in animals.

3-MINUTE EVIDENCE
Drugs and poisons are often
changed by the body after
being taken in a process
known as biotransformation.
Diamorphine, found in
heroin, is changed rapidly
(2–6 minutes) to form
6-monoacetylmorphine,
which is then transformed
(6–25 minutes) into the
pain-killer morphine.
Detecting morphine in
blood or urine does not
automatically mean that
morphine has been
consumed; diamorphine
or the pain-killer codeine,
which also forms morphine,
could also have been taken.

Humans and animals know from experience and instinct that some substances are highly dangerous and are to be avoided. Some toxic substances can cause specific effects, harm or death very quickly (acute toxicity) and some over a longer time (chronic toxicity). Toxicity can occur after exposure to amounts so small we cannot see them while other substances, not often considered toxic, may cause harm or death only at very high doses. The degree of harm also depends on the exposure route (toxic substances can be inhaled, ingested, injected or pass directly through skin) and other factors including the general health of the individual before exposure. A forensic toxicologist identifies substances, most commonly drugs, alcohol and other toxins, present in biological samples such as urine and blood serum, calculates the amount present and submits their report to the police or court. They may estimate when exposure might have occurred and be asked to interpret their findings and estimate the likely effects of the substances found. Morbid (post-mortem) toxicology involves the investigation of samples from the dead, such as sudden, unexplained deaths or fatal accidents from drinking a lethal substance. Criminal (antemortem) toxicology involves investigation of samples taken from the perpetrators or victims of a crime, such as murders, assaults, drug-assisted sexual assaults and road-traffic offences.

RELATED TOPICS
See also
AUTOPSY
page 14

DRUGS
page 90

3-SECOND BIOGRAPHIES
PARACELSUS
1493–1541
Swiss-German physician
considered to be the 'father' of
the formal study of toxicology

MATHIEU ORFILA
1787–1853
French toxicologist who served
as an expert witness in many
high-profile criminal cases

ALICE HAMILTON
1896–1970
American physician, expert in
occupational medicine and
Harvard's first female professor
who studied toxic effects of
many substances on workers
exposed to them and
campaigned successfully for
safe working conditions

30-SECOND TEXT
Craig McKenzie

Toxins can be detected from blood, urine and saliva. Hair can reveal long-term drug use.

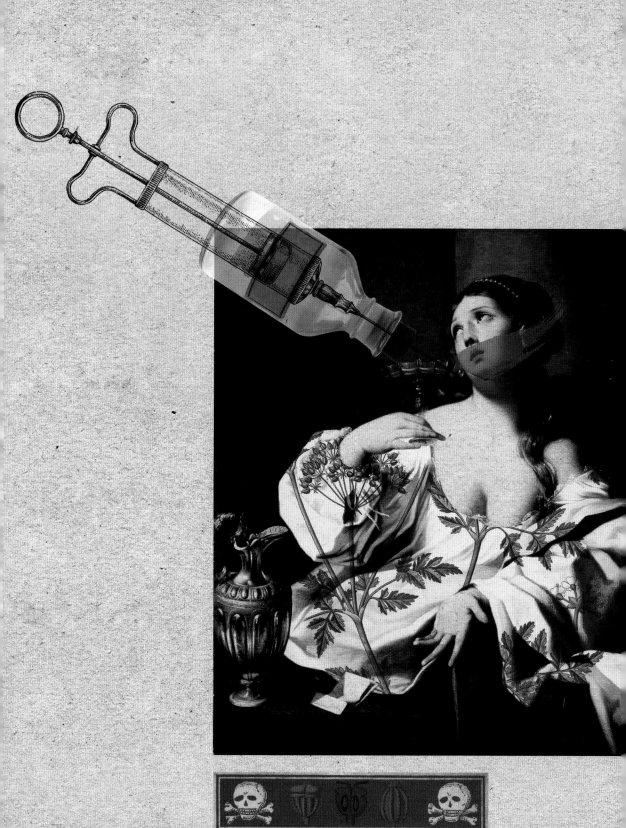

EXPLOSIVES

the 30-second scenario

Explosive materials have been known since the ninth century with the invention of black powder by the Chinese and were developed commercially for the mining and munitions industries since the mid-1800s. Explosives can be categorized as materials that either detonate (sometimes called high explosives, for example Trinitrotoluene-TNT) or which deflagrate (often called low explosives, for example, most fireworks). The difference between the two is the speed at which the energy generated from the chemical or physical reaction expands outwards from the material. Explosives can also be categorized according to their sensitivity or how easy it may be to cause the explosive reaction. Primary explosives are very sensitive to stimuli such as shock, heat, electrical current or pressure, whereas secondary explosives are much more stable. Explosions follow an 'explosive train' made up (in its simplest form) of an initiator, a detonator and a main charge. A small amount of primary explosive such as mercury fulminate (the detonator) is initiated by, for example, an electrical current (the initiator) causing a contained high explosive, such as TNT, (the main charge) into which the detonator is placed, to react and explode. Timing devices, triggers or other explosive boosters are also often used.

3-SECOND CLUE
A wide variety of materials can be categorized as explosive, largely because of the amount of energy they release when they react either chemically or physically.

3-MINUTE EVIDENCE
The analysis of explosive residues involves collecting samples either from the scene of an explosion, from the remains of the explosive device, from the skin or clothing of a person or from the environment where an explosive device is thought to have been prepared. There is a wide range of chemicals being used in the production of improvised explosive devices (IEDs) and homemade explosive devices (HEDs) encountered in forensic casework, often making their identification challenging.

RELATED TOPICS
See also
EXPERT WITNESS
page 138

ADMISSIBILITY
page 142

EVIDENCE INTERPRETATION
page 148

EVIDENCE PRESENTATION
page 150

3-SECOND BIOGRAPHY
ALFRED NOBEL
1833–96
Swedish chemist, known for inventing dynamite and establishing the Nobel prizes

30-SECOND TEXT
Niamh Nic Daéid

Chemical presumptive tests for explosives result in a colour reaction indicating the presence of particular chemical bonds which suggest that specific explosives compounds may be present. Such tests are often used in the field.

THIS WAS CALLED THE "PICTURE OF THE CENTURY" WHEN TAKEN ON THE MORNING OF JUNE 5, 1901, WHEN THE MARE ISLAND AMMUNITION DEPOT POWDER MAGAZINE BLEW UP. THERE WERE NO CASUALTIES, BUT CONSIDERABLE PROPERTY DAMAGE RESULTED IN BOTH MARE ISLAND AND VALLEJO.

THEREOF. AND SHE WAS TAKING FOR RAIDERS RUN TO SAN FRANCISCO. THE COMPANY SUPPLIED A PUBLICITY SHOT OF THE FREBBIE COMING DOWN THE CHANNEL IN THE EARLY MORNING SUNLIGHT AFTER LEAVING DRY TABLEAU DOCK AT 7:00 A.M.

HERMAN'S CAMERA WAS POINTED DIRECTLY ACROSS STRAIT FROM THE

NATURAL SCIENCE EVIDENCE

NATURAL SCIENCE EVIDENCE
GLOSSARY

bioterrorism The use of infectious agents or biohazards as weapons of terrorism.

bryophytes A group of plants that include mosses, liverworts and hornworts.

clandestine grave Refers to a hidden burial or where an attempt has been made to conceal a burial.

Convention of International Trade in Endangered Species of Flora or Fauna (CITES) A treaty to protect endangered plants and animals.

dendrological analysis Detailed analysis of timber used as botanical evidence to identify the tree species, age, grain pattern and planing marks.

Lindbergh Law In 1932 American aviator Charles Lindbergh's 20-month-old son was abducted. The child's body was found two months later. This case was responsible for the Federal Kidnapping Act, popularly referred to as the Lindbergh Law.

magnetometry Measuring and mapping patterns of magnetism in the soil.

methamphetamine A highly addictive synthetic drug, also known as 'meth' or 'crystal meth'.

microbial forensics The application of scientific techniques to the analysis of evidence related to bioterrorism and crimes involving microorganisms.

microscopy The utilization of microscopes to view objects too small to be seen by the naked eye.

morphology A branch of biology concerned with the study of shape, form and structure.

palynomorphs Microscopic airborne objects including, for example, pollen, spores, dust and fungi. Palynomorphs may be plant or animal structures that are microscopic in size (from about 5μm to about 500μm).

plant taxon The classification of one or more populations of a plant organism.

radiocarbon dating A method to determine the age of an object that contains organic material using the properties of radio carbon.

voucher specimen Any specimen that serves as a basis of study and is retained as a reference.

FORENSIC BOTANY

the 30-second scenario

3-SECOND CLUE
Forensic botany is the
application of plant
sciences to criminal
or civil investigations.

3-MINUTE EVIDENCE
In the murder case of
Denise Johnson in 1992,
whose body was found in
the desert near Phoenix,
Arizona, USA, forensic
botanical evidence linked
the murderer's pickup truck
to the scene of the crime.
This was the first case in
which botanical DNA
analysis was used to match
an individual tree at the
scene with seed pods
recovered from the
suspect. Forensic botany
can also be applied to
trace the provenance of
foodstuffs, and stolen or
smuggled goods, including
illegally traded timber,
and is used to help solve
environmental crimes,
which are an increasing
threat to natural resources.

An estimated 400,000 species of
plants exist on Earth, and seeds, flowers, stems
and leaf material can provide information about
a particular place. Forensic botanists may attend
a crime scene to carry out a botanical survey,
gather evidence, provide intelligence on priority
areas to search, and perform identification and
analysis of plant samples recovered from items
such as tools, footwear, vehicles or clothing.
They may be asked to recreate an outdoor
environment from which a questioned sample
may have originated or to testify as expert
witnesses in court. Botanical evidence can also be
used to identify clandestine graves. When soil is
disturbed, certain plants invade the fresh surface
quickly while others may follow in succession until
the area recovers. However, the composition and
distribution of the new assemblage often does not
match the original plant community. The presence
of a buried body may also chemically alter the soil
and either promote or inhibit plant growth. As
a result, the area that has been dug will be at a
different stage of growth than its surroundings:
this distinction may be visible for decades after
disturbance. Forensic botanists can also examine
a victim's digestive tract to obtain information
about their last meal. Using the known digestive
rates of plant-based foods, it may be possible
to estimate the time that passed between the
consumption of the last meal and death.

RELATED TOPICS
See also
FORENSIC PALYNOLOGY
page 106

FORENSIC SOIL SCIENCE
page 112

3-SECOND BIOGRAPHIES
'ÖTZI'
C. 3345–3300 BCE
A 5,200-year-old frozen corpse
discovered in 1991 in the Italian
Alps. Fragments of six species
of bryophytes found in Ötzi's
digestive tract shed light on his
lifestyle and final days

ARTHUR KOEHLER
1885–1967
American expert on wood
anatomy and identification
whose dendrological analysis of
a homemade ladder led to the
conviction of Bruno Hauptmann
in the Lindbergh kidnapping

30-SECOND TEXT
Lorna Dawson

*Plants can help to
establish the likelihood
that a particular species
came from a specific
site, perhaps the scene
of a crime.*

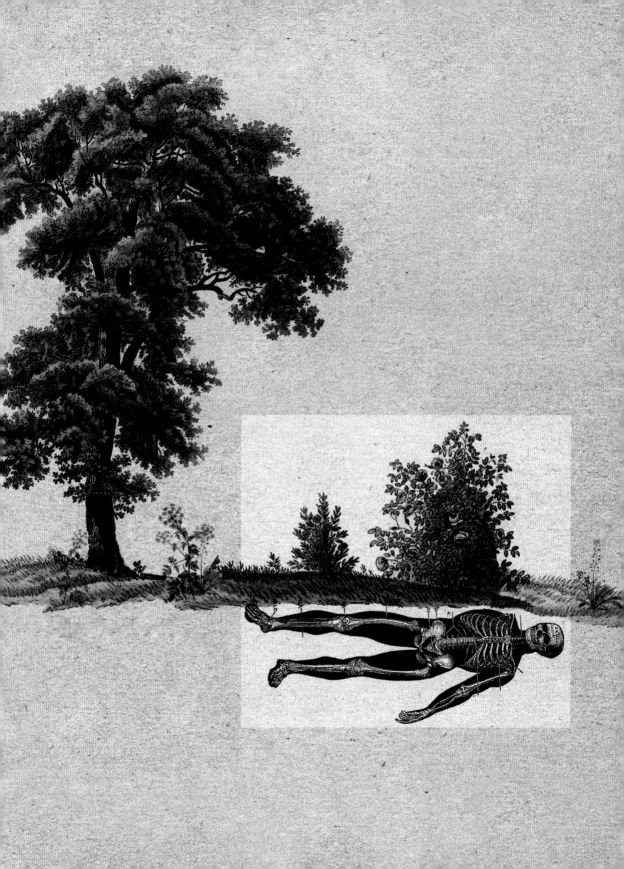

FORENSIC ENTOMOLOGY

the 30-second scenario

Evolution has allowed insects to attain a wide diversity in both form and development. Through the science of forensic entomology some organisms can tell us a great deal about when a crime was committed and how long a body has been dead. Forensic entomology focuses on the necrophagous (or carrion-feeding) insects that typically infest human remains. As the body decomposes, certain insects and invertebrates colonize the cadaver in a sequential and measured rate. The identification of insect species associated with a cadaver, and knowledge of the actual stages of development of particular species, can help ascertain the state of decomposition and subsequently the approximate time since death. The main species of interest to forensic entomologists are blowflies and beetles, which undergo a complete or 'holometabolous' development, with stages including eggs, hatching, growth, shedding and pupal. Entomological evidence may also help to determine how a person has died, or whether the body has been moved or disturbed post-mortem. The action of insect mouthparts during feeding can produce wounds that may be misinterpreted as previous abuse injuries and so care is advocated in terms of interpretation.

RELATED TOPICS
See also
TIME DEATH INTERVAL
page 26

FORENSIC PALYNOLOGY
page 106

FORENSIC SOIL SCIENCE
page 112

3-SECOND BIOGRAPHIES
SUNG TZ'U
1188–1251
Author of *The Washing Away of Wrongs* (1247) in which he describes one of the first uses of forensic entomology: a case in which flies were attracted to a sickle used to commit murder

JEAN PIERRE MÉGNIN
1828–1905
French entomologist whose books *La Faune des Tombeaux* (1887) and *La Faune des Cadavres* (1894) rank among the most important on forensic entomology. The second contains work on the theory of predictable waves, or successions of insects on corpses

30-SECOND TEXT
Lorna Dawson

Insects found on corpses can be used to estimate when death occurred.

WILDLIFE

the 30-second scenario

Many iconic species have either become extinct or are on the verge of extinction due to the illegal trade in wildlife, with ivory, rhino horn and tiger parts being the most high-profile examples. Rhino horn alone sells for $95,000 per kilogram on the black market, more than double the price of gold; the illegal trade in elephant ivory led to more than 20,000 animals being slaughtered in Africa in 2016; and the trade in tiger parts has already led to the extinction of four of the eight subspecies in the last 50 years. Trade is monitored by CITES (the Convention of International Trade in Endangered Species of Flora or Fauna). Forensic techniques, including morphology, microscopy and DNA, assist in the enforcement of legislation. Forensic testing is mainly used to determine the species. For example, if a large tusk is present a morphological examination may suffice to establish whether it originated from an elephant, and is not that of a narwhal or a tooth from a hippopotamus. Seized samples are often fragmented and in these circumstances DNA analysis can be used. A DNA sequence from a seized sample can be compared with a known sample (called a voucher specimen) to report a confident association. These samples are normally held by zoos or museums and are also available on an internet database called GenBank.

3-SECOND CLUE
The illegal trade in wildlife is a major criminal activity leading to the extinction of many iconic species, yet is rarely a focus of mainstream forensic investigations.

3-MINUTE EVIDENCE
When a shipment of multiple ivory samples is confirmed as coming from an African elephant, for example, it can be possible to determine poaching hotspots where the elephants were killed. In much the same way that humans across the globe have slightly different DNA, so it is with many other species, including elephants. This forensic intelligence can first be used to determine if a large seizure is from one area, and can aid in anti-poaching efforts.

RELATED TOPICS
See also
DNA PROFILING
page 36

HAIR COMPARISON
page 58

3-SECOND BIOGRAPHY
SAMUEL WASSER
c. 1954–
Research professor at the University of Washington who has been central to the DNA typing of elephants and development of a DNA database

30-SECOND TEXT
Adrian Linacre

Forensic tests can determine whether body parts purported to be from one species are in fact from an endangered one. Trade in animal skins, ivory, horn and other parts remains a billion-dollar global business, despite condemnation and campaigning.

FORENSIC PALYNOLOGY

the 30-second scenario

Forensic palynology has been used as a tool for more than 50 years and involves the characterization of pollen and spores in the context of the criminal justice system. Pollen and spores can be obtained from an extremely wide range of items, including human bodies, and can provide information as to the place where the items last came into contact and the characteristics of the source environments. Their usefulness lies in a combination of their abundance, varied dispersal mechanisms, their resistance to both mechanical and chemical destruction, microscopic size and morphology. Their complex morphology often permits identification to an individual parent plant taxon that can be used to deduce a specific ecological habitat or a specific scene. Pollen and spore assemblages characterize different environments and scenes and can be picked up easily and transported away from scenes of interest without providing any visual evidence of transfer. Forensic palynologists may attend a crime scene to carry out a survey of the plant species at the scene and its surroundings, collect evidence and provide intelligence on priority areas to search, and perform identification and analysis of plant samples recovered from objects such as footwear, tools, vehicles or clothing.

3-SECOND CLUE
Forensic palynology is the use of pollen or spores to aid criminal investigations by identifying the combination of plant species most likely to have been at, or near to, the last place a person visited.

3-MINUTE EVIDENCE
Palynomorphs – pollen, spores, dust, fungi and other airborne objects – are identified using a binocular microscope or a Scanning Electron Microscope (SEM). DNA can be extracted from the samples and analysed. DNA analysis of pollen in honey, for example, can be used to identify the plants that the bees visited and inform on environmental impacts of pesticides. Spores can also be used as evidence of the last place where an individual had breathed. Through careful sampling of the nasal passages, the pollen profile can reflect, literally, the last breath taken by a victim.

RELATED TOPICS
See also
TIME DEATH INTERVAL
page 26

FORENSIC BOTANY
page 100

FORENSIC SOIL SCIENCE
page 112

3-SECOND BIOGRAPHIES
LENNART VON POST
1884–1951
Swedish naturalist and geologist who outlined the use of pollen in case work. He was the first to publish a quantitative analysis of pollen

DALLAS MILDENHALL
1944–
One of the most insightful forensic palynologists practising today. Based in New Zealand, his areas of expertise include palaeoclimatology, quaternary studies, biostratigraphic services, forensic palynology and paleoenvironmental analysis

30-SECOND TEXT
Lorna Dawson

Palynomorphs can be used to link individuals directly with the scene of a crime.

1860
Born in Edinburgh,
Scotland

1883
Graduates with a BA in
Natural Science from
Trinity College,
Cambridge

1884
Becomes Professor of
Biology at University
College, Dundee

1896
Expedition to Bering
Straits to assess the seal
fur industry

1898
Awarded Commander of
the Bath for his service
to fisheries

1917
Appointed to chair
of Natural History at
St Andrews University
the year in which he
publishes his seminal
work, *On Growth and
Form*

1918
Delivers Royal Institution
Christmas Lecture on 'The
Fish of the Sea'

1934
Becomes President of the
Royal Society of
Edinburgh

1937
Receives knighthood

1946
Awarded the Royal
Society Darwin Medal

1948
Dies at home in St
Andrews – he was still
teaching at the age of 87

D'ARCY WENTWORTH THOMPSON

D'Arcy Wentworth Thompson

was a university professor for 63 of his 88 years. He was a classic polymath, being a biologist, a mathematician and a classics scholar – one of the first biomathematicians.

When he took up the Chair at University College, Dundee it was to create a zoology museum for teaching and research. Thompson was a great communicator of science, being able to talk with ease to the smallest child and the greatest minds of the time alike. He was friendly with the Dundee whaling skippers and so was able to obtain many specimens from various places around the Arctic. He was also able to collect specimens personally when he was made commissioner for a joint British-American enquiry into the fur seal population in the Bering Sea. His final report drew attention not only to the decline in the number of fur seals but also to the near extinction of the sea otter and the threat to the whale population. He became one of the pioneers for conservation of species and for the issue of protection orders for those facing extinction.

On Growth and Form is unquestionably Thompson's greatest literary achievement and the first edition ran to nearly 800 pages. In it he pioneered the use of mathematics in biology. His focus was on the effect that size has on the shape of animals and plants. He also explored the logarithmic spiral of mollusc shells and animal horns and even the arrangements of leaves and other plant components. Most of the book was written in 1915 but with the deprivations of the First World War being felt heavily, it was not completed until 1917.

Thompson was not a great supporter of Darwinian Theory but preferred to explain our natural world through the predictability of mathematics. That is not to say that he rejected evolution, but he did not consider it to be the true driving force. How ironic that his book is widely held as the second greatest biology text ever written – after Darwin's *Origin of Species*! The text has gone through many new editions but has been in print for 100 years and celebrated its centenary in 2017.

Thompson was described as being 'tall, bearded, venerable and kindly with an incurable zest for life and adventure'. A spectacular orator and communicator, he was known to pull random objects from his pockets as a focus for his lectures, and once even talked with a live chicken under his arm.

Sue Black

FORENSIC ARCHAEOLOGY

the 30-second scenario

Forensic archaeology focuses on
locating and recovering buried human remains
and forensic evidence including weapons, drugs
or money in criminal investigations. Standard
archaeological techniques, such as landscape
survey, field walking, analysis of aerial imagery,
and use of historic and geological maps, help
to develop forensic search strategies to locate
mass graves and clandestine burials. Non-invasive
geophysical survey methods, including ground-
penetrating radar and magnetometry, are used
to detect remains once a likely area of burial has
been identified. Stratigraphic excavation strategies
– whereby deposited layers of soil, occupation
activity or debris, are removed in sequential order
from the most recent to oldest – are employed to
recover victims, prevent contamination of forensic
evidence and determine the sequence of events
associated with single burials, mass graves, mass
disaster events and fire scenes. Radiocarbon dating
assists with establishing the time interval since the
remains were buried and determining if bones are
archaeological or modern. The largely unwritten
distinction between 'forensic' and 'archaeological'
is 70 years before the present date – but this varies,
depending on the case. Forensic archaeologists
work closely with other professionals within the
criminal investigation framework to ensure that
the excavation procedure records and preserves
evidence accurately from the scene.

RELATED TOPICS
See also
FOOTWEAR MARKS
page 80

FIRE SCENE INVESTIGATION
page 88

FORENSIC PALYNOLOGY
page 106

FORENSIC SOIL SCIENCE
page 112

3-SECOND BIOGRAPHY
JOHN HUNTER
1949–
Pioneer of forensic archaeology
in the UK who co-authored the
first books on the subject and
has been fundamental to the
development of the discipline

30-SECOND TEXT
Diana Swales

3-SECOND CLUE
Forensic archaeology uses
traditional archaeological
approaches and techniques
for the location and
recovery of buried evidence
in criminal and humanitarian
investigations.

3-MINUTE EVIDENCE
Stratigraphy in archaeology
is the study of the
sequential relationship
between artefacts, natural
and man-made layers
and structures. Dating
evidence, such as coins
or expiry dates on food
wrappers, found within
a grave or deposits formed
before or after the burial
can help ascertain a
minimum and maximum
time limit within which
the burial occurred. This
helps in understanding
the formation process
of a crime scene and
maximizes body and
evidence recovery.

*Examples of the types
of evidence forensic
archaeologists
seek to preserve
include fibres, tyre
tracks, shoeprints
and DNA.*

FORENSIC SOIL SCIENCE

the 30-second scenario

Soil covers much of the earth's terrestrial surface and, especially wet, clayey or organic soils, can be transferred easily to anything or anyone moving over it. People come into contact with soil when they travel on foot or horseback, in vehicles, or dig in it – and they leave their mark. Ancient Romans learned from a visual examination of soil embedded in horses' hooves to establish where their enemies had travelled. Soil (or related geological material, oil and petrol) can originate from urban as well as rural environments, with traces from industrial or building processes adding to the information within the soil. Forensic soil scientists may attend a crime scene to collect evidence, provide intelligence on priority areas to search, and perform laboratory analysis of soil samples recovered from objects such as footwear, tools, vehicles or clothing. Inorganic analysis of minerals or chemical elements helps to ascertain the likely geological location of soil while organic analysis uses markers such as alkanes and alcohols or pollen characterization, to inform on land use and vegetation type present at a particular location. Through maps and soil databases, the painstaking work of forensic soil scientists can narrow down the search focus to areas that match the characteristics of the questioned soil sample. Soil scientists may also testify as expert witnesses in both criminal and civil cases.

3-SECOND CLUE
Examining soil samples involves identifying the likely provenance of the questioned samples and providing evidence of the likelihood that it came from a specific site, such as a crime scene.

3-MINUTE EVIDENCE
Apart from its value in linking individual suspects to crime scenes, or helping in searches, forensic soil science is also used to trace the provenance of drugs and other smuggled goods, including wildlife and explosives, and to aid in the reconstruction of war crimes. Its significance was highlighted in 1997 as part of the evidence that helped to prosecute suspects involved in the genocide of more than 8,000 Muslims from the town of Srebrenica in the former Yugoslavia.

RELATED TOPICS
See also
TIME DEATH INTERVAL
page 26

FORENSIC BOTANY
page 100

FORENSIC ENTOMOLOGY
page 102

FORENSIC PALYNOLOGY
page 106

3-SECOND BIOGRAPHIES
GEORG POPP
1861–1943
German chemist and the first investigator to use soil as evidence to solve a murder case

RAY MURRAY
1929–
Forensic geologist who wrote the first book on forensic geology and established the current analytical principles of forensic soil science using chemistry and mineralogy

30-SECOND TEXT
Lorna Dawson

Forensic soil scientists draw on biology, physics, chemistry, geology and ecology in murder, drugs and environmental cases.

STABLE ISOTOPE ANALYSIS

the 30-second scenario

3-SECOND CLUE
Every chemical molecule is made up of different ratios of stable isotopes of the atoms present; through analysis, they can be used to trace people's movements and provide information about the provenance of materials such as drugs and explosives.

3-MINUTE EVIDENCE
Stable isotope analysis is used to identify the origin of human remains, as in the case of the torso of a young boy found in the River Thames in London on 21 September 2001. Investigators established Benin in southwest Nigeria as his place of origin and he was subsequently named. Stable isotopes can also provide details of the methods used to produce explosives, synthetic drugs (methamphetamine, for example), and to establish the origin of some drugs (such as cocaine).

Stable isotopes are important markers of where material has come from, adding another layer of information to that of elemental analysis. Bones, soft tissue, hair, nails, teeth, as well as soil, water and foodstuffs can all be analysed across a range of stable isotopes – for example, carbon, nitrogen and hydrogen – and compared with scene samples or reference samples to help ascertain the likely origin. A map or isoscape is produced to show the isotopic signature in a particular geographical zone. This is most commonly used to establish the provenance of a skeleton, since bones and teeth are generally the human remains that remain intact the longest after death has occurred. In the absence of any other distinguishing features or evidence to help with victim identification, stable isotope profiles can provide useful information about a person's diet and geographic life history, assisting an investigation involving, for example, unidentified victims of mass disasters. Stable isotope profiles of hair and nails can yield information about a person's recent life circumstance up to around 15 months into their past. Since hair and nail samples can be collected relatively non-invasively, stable isotope profiles of these tissues may also be used to reveal information on recent geographic movement in the living. This information may prove useful to check on a suspect's statement about their movements.

RELATED TOPICS
See also
FORENSIC ANTHROPOLOGY
page 16

TIME DEATH INTERVAL
page 26

FORENSIC SOIL SCIENCE
page 112

3-SECOND BIOGRAPHY
JAMES EHLERINGER
1949–
American biologist who used stable isotopic analysis in the identification of drug-trafficking routes

30-SECOND TEXT
Lorna Dawson

Stable isotope analysis and other techniques that use the chemical profile of material including bones, teeth and soft tissue make it possible to identify the origin of victims of human trafficking or mass disasters.

DIGITAL RECORDS

DIGITAL RECORDS
GLOSSARY

analogue Using information, such as sound or images, that is stored or sent in a continuously changing form, for example, photographic film.

bitcoin A digital currency and payment system.

cryptography The art of solving codes.

cybercrime Attacks against computer systems and traditional crimes using the internet.

dark net An alternative part of the internet that is not visible and can only be accessed using specialist software. It is often used for the purposes of computer crime.

digital Information comprised of bits of data in the form sequences of ones and zeros.

GPS (Global Positioning System) Worldwide navigation system that provides location data based on satellite information.

Internet of Things/Digital Mesh Expression referring to the interconnection via the internet of everyday objects.

lossy compression The permanent loss of original data when a file is compressed.

malware Software that is designed to disrupt or damage.

metadata Data that describes and provides information about other data.

phishing An attempt to attain sensitive information for nefarious reasons.

ransomware attack Malicious computer code used to hold a computer system to ransom.

reverse engineer Reproduction of a product following a detailed examination of its construction.

zero-day attacks Exploitation of a previously unknown software vulnerability.

VIDEO ANALYSIS
the 30-second scenario

3-SECOND CLUE
Forensic video analysis
handles the use of video
in court as evidence, where
sometimes a crime has
been recorded, or the
suspects are filmed
entering or leaving a
crime scene.

3-MINUTE EVIDENCE
Surveillance footage of the
bombing of the Boston
Marathon in 2013 was
released to the public,
which sped up the task of
identifying and tracking
the movements of the two
brothers responsible for
the attack. Opportunities
for witnesses at crime
scenes to record events
in real time are also
rising exponentially as
smartphones become a
universal fixture and their
recordings can be swiftly
uploaded or broadcast
to social media.

Despite some concerns over civil liberties, being 'caught on camera' in public arenas is commonplace. Dashboard cameras in cars as well as bodycams are also increasingly common and important in providing supporting evidence in investigations. As the number of CCTV systems expands and the quality of their images improves, so do opportunities for video recordings to be used as forensic evidence. Image quality, however, is often limited due to resolution, lighting and compression. Loss of detail can be a factor with digital video, because of lossy (irreversible) compression. For investigation purposes, image-enhancement software can afford some improvement of quality, and contrast-enhancement filters may improve detail. Video is used, for example, to compare a suspect with a person on a recording to match face, clothing, posture or gait; or to determine vehicle speed, particularly in cases of collisions between vehicles. Forensic investigation can be conducted to find proof of tampering with video recordings which, done professionally, is not easy to detect. For example, partially erased video files can sometimes be recovered by using software to analyse the composition of the file. If the header, which contains metadata (information with properties such as size of the recording) of the video file is missing, a new header can be added to play the recording.

RELATED TOPICS
See also
FACIAL IMAGE COMPARISON
page 46

IMAGE ANALYSIS
page 124

DIGITAL DEVICES
page 128

30-SECOND TEXT
Zeno Geradts

Public surveillance is a fact of modern life as security cameras are now standard fixtures in shopping malls, mass transit stations, petrol stations, car parks, and in hotel, bank and office foyers.

AUDIO

the 30-second scenario

As with other forms of electronic evidence, such as images from phones, there is an increasing amount of recorded sound in the contemporary world. Forensic audio analysis is usually focused on voice recordings but can have other applications, for example, the recognition of gun shots and music samples. Recordings can be made in analogue or digital form although the latter has largely replaced the former. There are many proprietary formats of digital recording, each employing its own compression and decompression program. Compression of a recording will result in some loss of data that may compromise the quality of the evidence. Forensic audio analysis can be used to detect editing of a recording in cases of alleged tampering. There is a range of methods to detect editing including analysis of background electronic signals and the electrical network, for instance noise generated by mains-powered devices in close proximity to the recording device can provide vital forensic evidence to the investigation. Forensic speaker recognition can be used to distinguish one speaker from another based on the recorded material available. Many recordings, such as voice mail or telecommunications interceptions, have significant audible background noise rendering the voice recording unintelligible. Speech enhancement will improve the speech at the expense of the background noise.

3-SECOND CLUE
Forensic audio analysis is the investigation of recorded audio including voice recordings and ambient and background noise, and usually requires enhancement, suppression and disaggregation of the range of noises present.

3-MINUTE EVIDENCE
The increased digitization of the human world also increases the opportunity to record human activity, both incidentally and deliberately. This includes the opportunity to record not just voices and the messages they carry but also the ambient audible noise and the sub-audible background noise generated by the environment. All of this information can be exploited by forensic analysis.

RELATED TOPIC
See also
DIGITAL DEVICES
page 128

3-SECOND BIOGRAPHIES
CATALIN GRIGORAS
fl. c. 1994
Director of the National Center for Media Forensics at the University of Colorado Denver. His research into digital signal processing has resulted in advanced methods to authenticate digital audio/video recordings and semiautomatic systems for forensic speaker recognition

JOHN H. L. HANSEN
1959–
American professor who established the Center for Robust Speech Systems at the University of Texas at Dallas, which focuses on research in speech processing, hearing sciences and language technologies

30-SECOND TEXT
Paul Reedy

Sound recordings may be used as admissible evidence in criminal cases such as fraud, accidents and slander.

IMAGE ANALYSIS

the 30-second scenario

3-SECOND CLUE
Forensic image analysis relates to the use of digital images in court from many sources, such as smartphones, ID documents and downloaded images.

3-MINUTE EVIDENCE
The main areas evaluated during picture analysis are: shadows, to evaluate how objects in the picture relate to the light source; eyes, to compare how the colours respond to light direction; the file data, which can often include GPS position and time; and reflections to determine whether they are coherent in the image.

Images are often used in court as supporting evidence, with examples often coming from cameras including smartphones, as well as being transferred via the internet. Forensic image analysis is often used to authenticate, enhance and compare the images. Image quality can be limited due to resolution, lighting and compression. Loss of detail is also a factor with digital images because of lossy (irreversible) compression. For investigation purposes, image-enhancement software can afford some improvement of quality, and contrast-enhancement filters may improve detail. Image analysis is frequently used in the investigation of identity documents or biometric comparison – in which people's physical details are analysed. Two images may be compared to determine whether the person is the same, different or has common characteristics. Questions relating to image tampering are often considered; in these cases, investigation based on the content of the image can be used to determine whether the image has been altered. Based on irregularities in the image sensor, it is also possible to determine if an image has been taken with a specific camera – sometimes referred to as the 'fingerprint' of the device.

RELATED TOPICS
See also
FACIAL IMAGE COMPARISON
page 46

VIDEO ANALYSIS
page 120

DIGITAL DEVICES
page 128

3-SECOND BIOGRAPHY
JESSICA FRIDRICH
1964–
Czech-born professor who developed data-hiding applications. Based at the University of Binghamton, New York, she was the first to publish on methods for using the weak sensor fingerprints in forensic science to determine if an image has been taken with a certain camera. This method is useful for many cases, including those involving producers of illicit images

30-SECOND TEXT
Zeno Geradts

Digital image analysis techniques are a form of biometrics which may be used in security systems for facial recognition.

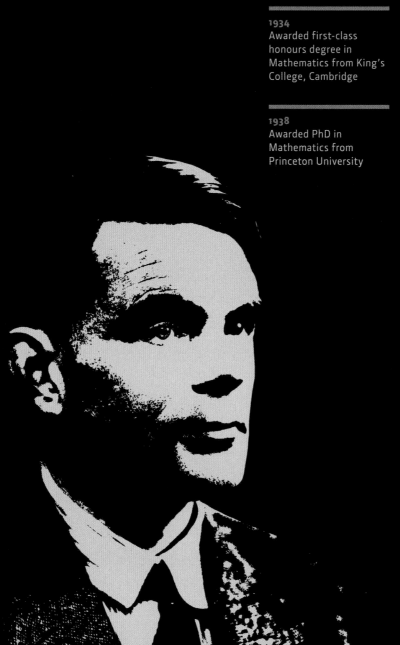

1912
Born in London, England

1934
Awarded first-class honours degree in Mathematics from King's College, Cambridge

1938
Awarded PhD in Mathematics from Princeton University

1946
Awarded an OBE for wartime services

1948
Appointed Reader in Mathematics at University of Manchester

1951
Elected Fellow of the Royal Society

1952
Prosecuted for homosexual acts

1954
Commits suicide by cyanide poisoning

2013
Receives posthumous royal pardon

ALAN TURING

Alan Turing made an enormous contribution to the development of computer science and cryptography. He was recognized early on in childhood as a gifted mathematician and his academic development at Cambridge University and subsequently at Princeton confirmed this. Prior to completing his PhD he was already undertaking research work into the development of computing and the underpinning arithmetic upon which computers were based.

During the Second World War, Turing was based at Bletchley Park, the secret location of British codebreakers in Buckinghamshire, and there he played a leading part in the breaking of the German Enigma ciphers. Enigma machines were electrically driven cipher machines that operated by keying in a message at a keyboard where each keystroke would cause a rotor to move sequentially and a different letter to be outputted. The more rotors used, the more complicated the encryption. A further layer of encryption was also introduced using a plug board which linked and transposed pairs of letters prior to scrambling by the rotor series. Daily encryption keys would set the parameters such as the starting positions of the rotors, the order of their deployment and the letter pairs on the plug board. During his time at Bletchley Park, Turing and his colleagues were instrumental in creating mathematical methods that, combined with a decoding instrument (called a Bombe), were used to crack the Enigma code.

Following the Second World War, Turing worked on the development of an automatic computing engine at the National Physical Laboratory (NPL) and later in Manchester where he began to develop his ideas in artificial intelligence proposing the 'Turing test' to determine a machine's ability to demonstrate intelligent behaviour. The test requires that a person cannot distinguish between a computer and a human being based on the answers provided to a set of questions. A computer is deemed to have passed the Turing test if the answers it provides mimic human responses to a set of questions. In the later years of his life, Turing also became very interested in modelling and understanding the patterns and models in biological systems that formed the basis of mathematical biology. The importance of being able to decipher patterns in data has become a cornerstone to the interpretation and evaluation of forensic evidence within a criminal or civil case.

The final years before Turing's death were marred by personal tragedy as he was arrested for homosexual behaviour, which was illegal in 1952, a charge to which he pled guilty. This meant that his security clearance was revoked and he could no longer continue his cryptography work with the security services. In 2013 he was posthumously pardoned by Queen Elizabeth.

Niamh Nic Daéid

DIGITAL DEVICES

the 30-second scenario

3-SECOND CLUE
Every digital device with a chip can be traced and this includes smartphones, computers and cars. Information can be stored in many formats and may include appointments, emails and messages.

3-MINUTE EVIDENCE
A notable case relating to data analysis is that of the terrorist Syed Farook, who shot 14 people dead in San Bernardino, California, in 2015. The FBI required access to an iPhone owned by the gunman to learn more about his movements that day. This required Apple to reverse engineer a new piece of software that would circumvent the maximum of ten password attempts; Apple argued that this violated their First Amendment right. The case was stopped after the FBI found another means to access the information required.

Nowadays, nearly all crimes will involve digital evidence. Digital traces are found in any device with a microchip, from smartphones and computers to medical devices, car electronics and many more. New hard- and software is continually developed by manufacturers at a rapid pace. The challenge in digital evidence is to gain access to the stored information within the various digital devices. Forensic laboratories regularly receive damaged or partially destroyed digital devices; by recovering the chip, they can sometimes recover data. Making the data readable is also a challenge and often, if the data is encrypted, brute-force dictionary attacks are required to gain access to the data through guessing passwords. Manufacturers of apps and devices also store their data in proprietary formats which makes it necessary to have information on the formats and how they are stored. Since these are often not readily available, reverse-engineered solutions to gather the information are sometimes needed. If recovery is possible, the interpretation of data in relation to the crime can proceed. Issues, such as tampering with the evidence, should be considered and clear questions given to the forensic investigator. Big-data analysis tools might help to assist the investigator to ask the relevant questions and find the virtual needle in the digital haystack.

RELATED TOPICS
See also
VIDEO ANALYSIS
page 120

IMAGE ANALYSIS
page 124

3-SECOND BIOGRAPHY
EOGHAN CASEY
fl. 2010–
Irish forensic scientist who has delivered expert testimony in civil and criminal cases, and has submitted expert reports and prepared trial exhibits for computer forensic and cybercrime cases. He has written several books on the topic of digital evidence

30-SECOND TEXT
Zeno Geradts

The recovery and analysis of evidence held on digital devices is a key aspect of forensic work relating to online crime or cyber security incidents.

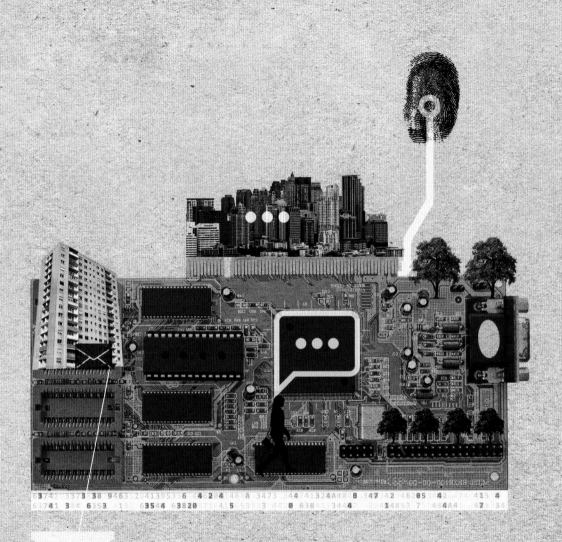

INTERNET
the 30-second scenario

Globally more than 3.5 billion people are now connected via the internet using mobiles, computers and other electrical devices. The sharing of child pornography is one of the most investigated internet crimes. The use of the 'dark net' enables restricted access between peer-to-peer file sharing, making it increasingly difficult for law enforcement to investigate. The trade of illegal drugs is seen on the internet and the use of anonymous money, such as bitcoins, makes it easier to conduct transactions and more difficult to link the trade and the persons involved. Financial crime is common when usernames and passwords are stolen and since many individuals use the same network for different accounts, their personal and financial security is at risk. Phishing emails and malware on PCs and mobile devices can complete transactions without the user's permission; often these attacks are only possible for a short period of time since financial institutions use cybersecurity measures to prevent them. Ransomware attacks are on the increase where the user has to pay bitcoins, or other money that cannot be tracked, to regain access to their files, data and operating systems. So-called zero-day attacks exploit security flaws in computer systems. Attacks are possible on public infrastructure, such as electricity and water supplies, and are often seen as cybercrime or, depending on scale, cyber war or cyberterrorism.

3-SECOND CLUE
Crimes conducted using the internet are evolving in today's society with incidents such as theft, stolen passwords and ransomware attacks commonly seen in cyber forensic investigations.

3-MINUTE EVIDENCE
The ability to gain unauthorized access to data in a system or computer – also known as 'hacking' – is becoming increasingly common. Kevin Mitnick, one of the first to be convicted for hacking, was arrested by the FBI in his home in North Carolina in 1995. Mitnick was charged with federal offences relating to a two and-a-half-year period of computer hacking, which included computer and wire fraud. Mitnick was convicted and banned from accessing the internet for two years. He now works as a security consultant.

RELATED TOPICS
See also
VIDEO ANALYSIS
page 120

IMAGE ANALYSIS
page 124

DIGITAL DEVICES
page 128

CYBER
page 132

3-SECOND BIOGRAPHY
TIMOTHY BERNERS-LEE
1955–
British engineer and computer scientist who is credited with the development of the World Wide Web as an information space in 1989

30-SECOND TEXT
Zeno Geradts

Cybercrime, malware and other attacks on the internet are often international and the attackers' identities concealed, making it difficult for crimes to be proved in a court of law.

CYBER

the 30-second scenario

Computers and the internet are now ubiquitous in most human endeavours. They are so interwoven with our lives, that the 'Internet of Things' and more recently the 'Digital Mesh' are descriptions applied to the global networked system. Digital evidence is in the form of ones and zeros that are constructed into a language that is used by devices, such as smartphones, and the network. It can also be intercepted when devices are communicating. Despite each connected entity having its own proprietary platform and language, and perhaps also being encrypted, events can be deciphered and interpreted to provide a meaning. Decoded, the language tells a story of the interactions, decisions and events that have occurred in which the network and the internet have been involved. The evidence can be in the form of GPS data on a mobile phone or intrusion into the secure network of a business or government organization for the purposes of spying or stealing intellectual property. Cybercrimes can include child sexual exploitation, intellectual-property theft, state-based and industrial espionage, financial theft, planting of evidence and false information, human trafficking, cyberbullying, identity theft, ideology, disruption and sabotage, and hate crimes.

RELATED TOPICS
See also
DIGITAL DEVICES
page 128

INTERNET
page 130

VALIDITY
page 140

EVIDENCE INTERPRETATION
page 148

3-SECOND BIOGRAPHY
KEVIN ASHTON
1968–
British technology pioneer who coined the term 'Internet of Things'

30-SECOND TEXT
Paul Reedy

The forensic science approach to cybercrime is one that uses detection, recovery, comparison, interpretation and communication of recovered digital evidence within the investigation or court room.

3-SECOND CLUE
Any activity that a person has online will leave a digital trace; cyber forensics investigates crimes that involve a computer and a network, usually the internet.

3-MINUTE EVIDENCE
Every interaction of each individual, every physical place they go, every transaction in which they engage can, theoretically, leave a digital record. A person engaging in criminal activity will do the same and this recording forms evidence to tell the story of what happened. Equally, it can exclude persons from any involvement. Experts using specialist tools preserve and analyse the data to provide a real-world meaning.

THE LAW & SCIENCE

THE LAW & SCIENCE
GLOSSARY

activity level propositions A proposition that suggests that a particular activity has occurred, for example, that an individual has broken a window.

Alford plea In US law, an Alford plea is a guilty plea where the defendant still maintains their innocence. A defendant will enter an Alford plea when they deny the crime but admit that the prosecution's evidence would be likely to convince a judge or jury of their guilt.

ancillary information Extra information.

feature-comparison method A method that systematically compares the physical features between two or more samples of a particular material including, for example, footwear marks, fingerprints or tool marks.

Kalisher Lecture An annual lecture by the Criminal Bar Association in the UK given in memory of the lawyer Michael Kalisher QC (1944–96).

prejudicial evidence Evidence that if introduced into court could unduly influence or bias a jury's decision making.

probative evidence Evidence that is introduced to the court intending to prove or establish facts.

source level propositions A proposition that suggests that a particular piece of evidence comes from a particular source, for example, that a piece of glass recovered from the clothing of a suspect comes from a specific broken window.

supposition A belief that is held without certain knowledge or proof.

systolic blood pressure deception test A test that is based on a suggestion that blood pressure is influenced by the emotional state of the individual and as such can be used to detect whether someone is lying. Deception tests are not universally accepted as scientifically valid.

EXPERT WITNESS

the 30-second scenario

Expert witnesses are called to court to provide testimony that must give additional insight or information outside the experience or knowledge expected from the jury, who are the triers of fact in a case. The expert witness must not usurp the role of the jury and their evidence must be probative and not prejudicial. Expert witnesses can be called by both the prosecution and the defence, however their overriding duty is to assist the court using their expertise and to be impartial and unbiased. The first likely expert witness used in a civil trial was a civil engineer, John Smeaton, in 1782. He was asked to give his opinion on why the harbour at Wells-next-the-sea in Norfolk, England, had silted to such an extent that it could no longer be used. He opined that the reclamation of the coastal marshlands and the erection of embankments by landowners were responsible but his views were vehemently challenged by opposing lawyers and their experts. The presiding judge, Lord Mansfield, would have none of it and ruled: 'The cause of the decay of the harbour is a matter of science … on this, such men as Mr Smeaton alone can judge.'

RELATED TOPICS
See also
VALIDITY
page 140

ADMISSIBILITY
page 142

EVIDENCE INTERPRETATION
page 148

EVIDENCE PRESENTATION
page 150

3-SECOND BIOGRAPHY
ROY MEADOW
1933–
British paediatrician who gave evidence in the 1999 trial of Sally Clark who was wrongly convicted of murdering her two baby sons. Meadow gave erroneous probabilistic evidence and Clark's conviction was overturned in 2003; she died in 2007

30-SECOND TEXT
Sue Black & Niamh Nic Daéid

3-SECOND CLUE
An expert witness possesses specialized knowledge or skills that will assist a jury in reaching a decision based on the facts presented during legal proceedings.

3-MINUTE EVIDENCE
The testimony of the expert witness is often a highlight of a trial. Experts are the only witnesses allowed to provide opinion evidence in a case. Celebrity expert witnesses are not new and Sir Bernard Spilsbury (see page 20) was one of the best known of his time. Today his equivalent is probably Henry C. Lee, most famed for his evidence in the O. J. Simpson trial (1995) although Lee courted controversy in the Phil Spector trial (2007).

Expert witnesses must provide unbiased evidence to the court. Their key role is to convey their evidence clearly to the jury.

VALIDITY

the 30-second scenario

3-SECOND CLUE
For a technique, a method or a procedure in forensic science to be valid, it must be repeatable, reproducible and accurate.

3-MINUTE EVIDENCE
In 2016, the US Justice Department acknowledged that almost every hair examiner in an FBI unit gave flawed testimony by over-reporting on the validity of microscopic hair comparison. Of the 32 defendants who had been sentenced to death on this evidence type, 14 had been executed before this error was reported. An addendum to the 2016 PCAST report stated: 'studies do not address the validity and degree of reliability of hair comparison as a forensic feature-comparison method.'

In its broadest sense, validity refers to how well a scientific test or piece of research actually measures what it purports to, or how well it reflects the reality that it claims to represent. Many measurement techniques used in forensic science can demonstrate scientific validity as part of quality-control procedures. The analysis of DNA, drug and toxicological samples and fire debris analysis, for example, are all carried out using validated techniques. In recent years, however, a number of reports coming out of the USA in particular challenge the validity of many evidence types within forensic science, particularly those that rely on subjective rather than objective opinions. Bite-mark comparison and hair analysis are perhaps two evidence types that have come in for the harshest criticism. The President's Council of Advisors on Science and Technology (PCAST) reported in 2016 that bite-mark analysis was not scientifically valid and was unlikely ever to be validated. There is no evidence that human bite marks are unique, that the pattern transfers reliably onto human skin and there is no understanding of the distortion of bite marks on human skin. The National Academy of Science report in 2009 concluded that 'In numerous instances, experts diverge widely in their evaluations of the same bite mark evidence, which has led to questioning of the value and scientific objectivity of such evidence.'

RELATED TOPICS
See also
EXPERT WITNESS
page 138

ADMISSIBILITY
page 142

EVIDENCE INTERPRETATION
page 148

EVIDENCE PRESENTATION
page 150

3-SECOND BIOGRAPHY
RICHARD SOUVIRON
1937–
Dentist who gave evidence in the case against the serial murderer Ted Bundy in 1987. Bundy appealed against the first-degree murder convictions on the basis of the bite-mark evidence but it was rejected and he was executed by electric chair in Texas in 1989

30-SECOND TEXT
Sue Black & Niamh Nic Daéid

The importance of demonstrating that a scientific method is valid is critical to the admissibility of that evidence type in court.

ADMISSIBILITY

the 30-second scenario

For evidence to be relevant to a court case, a judge will decide whether it would assist the jury in their deliberations regarding support for, or against, the charges brought by the prosecution. The party introducing the evidence to the court must demonstrate that the source of the information is reliable, whether that relates to either the credibility of a witness or the methodology of a scientific technique. There is no strict test of admissibility in the UK and it is solely at the discretion of the judge. In other jurisdictions such as the USA there are tests of admissibility, the most well known of which is the Daubert test. The purpose of this test is to ensure that a method used by an expert witness in examining evidence adheres to sound scientific principles. It requires that the theory or technique is accepted by the scientific community, that it has been subject to peer review and publication, that it can be tested, that it has known or potential error rates and that the research was conducted independent of intention to prove or disprove. The credibility of the witness to be considered an 'expert' is at the discretion of the court.

3-SECOND CLUE
For evidence to be deemed admissible in a court of law, the judge must decide that it is both relevant and reliable.

3-MINUTE EVIDENCE
Daubert v Merrell Dow Pharmaceuticals Inc. (1993) was a US Supreme Court case that has gone on to determine standards for admitting expert testimony. The case was based on an action against Dow that a nausea-managing drug had caused serious birth defects. One of the concerns was that the plaintiffs' evidence was generated specifically to address the litigation and this brought expert testimony and admissibility into question.

RELATED TOPICS
See also
EXPERT WITNESS
page 138

VALIDITY
page 140

EVIDENCE INTERPRETATION
page 148

EVIDENCE PRESENTATION
page 150

3-SECOND BIOGRAPHY
WILLIAM MOULTON MARSTON
1893–1947
Lawyer who invented the 'systolic blood pressure deception test', a forerunner of the lie detector, first used in court to support the defence of James Alphonso Frye who had confessed to murdering Robert Brown in 1920. Frye retracted his admission, the test was administered and the results admitted into court. Later, the Appeals court ruled that the test and its results were not admissible as scientific evidence, and Frye served 18 years in prison

30-SECOND TEXT
Sue Black & Niamh Nic Daéid

Admissibility of evidence falls directly within the responsibilities of the judge in a trial.

1947
Born Roger John Laugharne Thomas in Cwmgiedd, Powys, Wales

1966
Earns a BA in Law from Trinity Hall, Cambridge

1969
Called to the Bar (Gray's Inn, London)

1984
Becomes Queen's Counsel

1996
Appointed High Court Judge and knighted

2003
Becomes Lord Justice of Appeal

2004
Made a Fellow of Trinity College, Cambridge

2008
Becomes Vice President of Queen's Bench Division

2011
Named President of Queen's Bench Division

2013
Made Lord Chief Justice of England and Wales and a life peer – Lord Thomas of Cwmgiedd

2018
Chancellor of Aberystwyth University

Counsel. He was a presiding Judge of the Wales and Chester Circuit and was lead Judge for the Commercial Court before being appointed a Lord Justice of Appeal. Prior to his post as Lord Chief Justice of England and Wales he was first Vice-President, and then President, of the Queen's Bench Division.

In England and Wales the title 'Lord Chief Justice' is given to the senior judge who presides over the Queen's Bench Division of the High Court. Since the passing of the Constitutional Reform Act 2005 the 'Chief' is also Head of the Judiciary of England and Wales, a role previously performed by the Lord Chancellor. The Chief is also President of the Courts of England and Wales and executes more than 400 statutory duties including representing the views of the Judiciary to Parliament, the deployment of Judges and the allocation of work in courts in England and Wales. The Chief is also the presiding judge in the criminal division of the Court of Appeal and Hamza and, in October 2016, he was one of the three judges who ruled on the use of the royal prerogative for the issue of notification in accordance with triggering Article 50 of the Treaty on European Union (the Lisbon Treaty) – Brexit. The Chief has also worked on a far-reaching and ambitious project to remodel the civil justice system in England and Wales.

Lord Thomas is a strong advocate of the use of forensic science within the criminal justice system and has made many rulings in which he has been supportive of a strong scientific underpinning of evidence and highly critical of poor practice. His Kalisher Lecture of 2014 was entitled 'Expert evidence: The future of forensic science in criminal trials', in which he stated that 'it [forensic science] matters to society … in ensuring that the innocent are not convicted of crimes they did not commit and that the perpetrators of serious crimes are brought to justice.' Lord Thomas retired from office in 2017.

Sue Black & Niamh Nic Daéid

COGNITIVE BIASES

the 30-second scenario

3-SECOND CLUE
Cognitive bias is
an umbrella term in
psychology and relates
to the effects of
outside influences or
preconceptions on
perception, judgment
and decision making.

3-MINUTE EVIDENCE
Cognitive bias in fingerprint
examination has probably
been more studied than in
any other forensic evidence
type. The susceptibility
to cognitive bias was
highlighted in the case
of Brandon Mayfield, a
lawyer from Oregon whose
fingerprints were incorrectly
identified by the FBI as
being those of the Madrid
train bomber in 2004
when a partial print had
been found on a bag
of detonators. A formal
apology and a financial
settlement ensued.

It is important to understand the effects of cognitive biases on decision making in forensic science and to be able to mitigate against them where necessary. Although there are many different types of cognitive biases, confirmation and contextual bias are probably the best recognized in forensic science. Confirmation bias occurs when hypotheses are tested by looking disproportionately for confirming evidence to support a predetermined theory, while potentially ignoring conflicting evidence. Contextual bias occurs when ancillary information unduly influences the outcome of a consideration, either consciously or subconsciously. Biases have been identified as a common thread in wrongful convictions. The case of the West Memphis Three illustrates how, despite overwhelming evidence, the investigators and prosecutors failed to see the warning signs that they were heading down the wrong path towards a miscarriage of justice. Questionable science, false confessions and evidence from jailhouse informants all provided information that confirmed the investigators' preconceptions and led to a wrongful conviction for the brutal murder and mutilation of three eight-year-old boys in 1994. The three accused entered Alford pleas while asserting that they were innocent and were released having served 18 years in prison.

RELATED TOPICS
See also
ADMISSIBILITY
page 142

EVIDENCE INTERPRETATION
page 148

EVIDENCE PRESENTATION
page 150

3-SECOND BIOGRAPHY
DANIEL KAHNEMAN
1934–
A Nobel laureate, Israeli-
American psychologist who is
highly regarded for his work on
the psychology of judgment
and decision making. He
established a cognitive basis
for common human errors that
can be attributed to biases

30-SECOND TEXT
Sue Black & Niamh Nic Daéid

*Our understanding
of cognitive bias
across the forensic
science disciplines
remains limited.*

EVIDENCE INTERPRETATION

the 30-second scenario

Forensic observations can take the form of corresponding and non-corresponding features between the recovered material and some reference material. Typically, a mark (left, say, by an object or a finger) shows correspondence with reference impressions; micro-traces, such as a glass fragment or a textile fibre, correspond physically and chemically to a reference sample, for example, a glass pane or a garment; or a DNA profile obtained from a biological stain corresponds to a reference DNA profile. However, correspondence doesn't establish that the recovered material came from a specific source or confirm that the material was transferred during the criminal activity. Evidence interpretation boils down to the answers to two generic questions: what is the probability of making the scientific observations if the reference sample (say, glass from a broken window at a crime scene) is the source of the questioned material (a fragment of glass found on a suspect's clothing); and, what is the probability of making the same scientific observations if an unknown object (any other broken window) is the source? These are called source level propositions. When the activities are in dispute the questions will be: what is the probability of making the observations if the activities alleged by the prosecution occurred, versus what is the probability of making the observations if the defence's account is true? These are called activity level propositions. Accounting for both sides of the coin ensures balance and fairness.

RELATED TOPICS
See also
EXPERT WITNESS
page 138

VALIDITY
page 140

ADMISSIBILITY
page 142

EVIDENCE PRESENTATION
page 150

3-SECOND BIOGRAPHY
IAN WEBBER EVETT
1943–
Senior consultant for the Forensic Science Service (UK) and a pioneer of evidence interpretation

30-SECOND TEXT
Christophe Champod

3-SECOND CLUE
Evidence interpretation is the formulation and communication of the meaning and strength of the results of forensic examinations in a candid and understandable manner, whether to the investigators or the court.

3-MINUTE EVIDENCE
Forensic observations must be interpreted in the context of the case being investigated. This interpretation adheres to some basic principles: first, the forensic scientist will assign probabilities associated with their observations, in the light of at least two different possible scenarios (propositions) that could explain the observations; second, only the probability of the observation given the propositions are considered; and third, the probabilities of the observation assigned in this way must be based on documented, accessible and reliable knowledge.

Evidence interpretation should adhere to sound scientific principles and be conveyed in terms of probabilities.

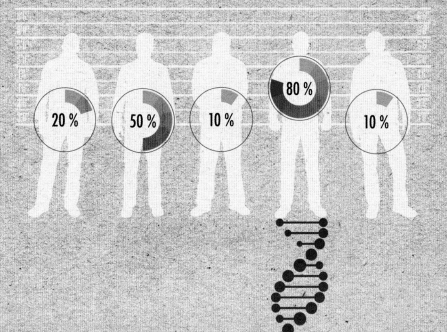

EVIDENCE PRESENTATION

the 30-second scenario

A case is often won or lost depending upon how effectively the evidence in the case was presented to the jury who are the triers of fact and whose responsibility it is to determine the guilt or innocence of the person on trial. Evidence that is submitted to a court must be relevant and probative and it cannot be based on supposition or hearsay or be prejudicial. There are many different ways in which evidence may be presented in court. These include eyewitness or expert witness testimony assisted by video footage, still photographs, exhibits, audio recordings, transcripts of conversations, maps, analytical results, drawings and written documents all called exhibits or productions. While the prosecuting legal team must present evidence to support their charges, the defence may choose not to present evidence as they must only prove doubt in the validity of the charges brought. If the defence choose to present evidence then the witnesses they call may not necessarily include the defendant. The prosecution cannot compel the defendant to give evidence. Evidentiary objections can be made by either legal team with regards to admissibility, and the judge must decide whether to sustain the objection or overrule it. For example, a lawyer can object to a line of questioning if the evidence is prejudicial and outweighs its probative value.

3-SECOND CLUE
Jurists are largely passive observers and during the course of a trial they will be presented with evidence from a number of witnesses, which they must utilize in their decision making.

3-MINUTE EVIDENCE
Evidence may be objected to in court if it is prejudicial. For example, a colour photograph of a murder victim may be so horrific that it does not serve to add any further probative value compared to other forms of evidence, but it is highly prejudicial as its inclusion is intended to shock the jurors. In so doing, the image may disproportionately inflame the jury to return a guilty verdict.

RELATED TOPICS
See also
VALIDITY
page 140

ADMISSIBILITY
page 142

EVIDENCE INTERPRETATION
page 148

3-SECOND BIOGRAPHIES
FRANCESCO BARBERINI
1597–1679
A graduate in canon and civil law who was made Grand Inquisitor of the Roman Inquisition. He was one of the three judges who did not sign for Galileo's imprisonment

BRENDA MARJORIE HALE
1945–
Justice of the Supreme Court, one of the most senior female judges in the history of the UK. The first woman in the UK to become president of the Supreme Court

30-SECOND TEXT
Sue Black & Niamh Nic Daéid

How forensic evidence is presented to the jury is critical to ensuring their understanding of the evidence.

APPENDICES

RESOURCES

BOOKS

'Criminal and Environmental Soil Forensics'
L. A. Dawson & R. W. Mayes in
Introduction to Environmental Forensics
Robert D. Morrison & Brian Murphy (eds)
(Academic Press, 3rd edn 2014)

Clarke's Analytical Forensic Toxicology
Adam Negrusz & Gail Cooper (eds)
(Pharmaceutical Press, 2nd edn 2013)

*Criminal Dismemberment: Forensic and
Investigative Analysis*
S. Black, G. Rutty, S. V. Hainsworth and
G. Thomson
(CRC Press 2017)

*Encyclopedia of Criminology and Criminal
Justice*
Gerben Bruinsma & David Weisburd (eds)
(Springer 2014)

Fingerprints and Other Ridge Skin Impressions
Christophe Champod, Chris Lennard, Pierre
Margot & Milutin Stoilovic
(CRC Press, 2nd edn 2016)

Forensic Approaches to Buried Remains
J. R. Hunter, B. Simpson & C. Sturdy Colls
(Wiley-Blackwell 2013)

Forensic Archaeology: A Global Perspective
W. J. M. Groen, N. Márquez-Grant &
R. C. Janaway
(Wiley-Blackwell 2015)

Forensic Botany: A Practical Guide
D. W. Hall & J. H. Byrd
(Wiley-Blackwell 2012)

Forensic Science in Wildlife Investigations
Adrian Linacre (ed.)
(CRC Press 2008)

*Foundations of Forensic Document Analysis:
Theory and Practice*
Michael J. Allen
(Wiley-Blackwell 2015)

An Introduction to Forensic Genetics
William Goodwin, Adrian Linacre & Sibte Hadi
(Wiley-Blackwell, 3rd edn 2018)

Microbial Forensics
B. Budowle, S. Schutzer, R. Breeze, P. Keim
& S. Morse (eds)
(Academic Press, 2nd edn 2010)

*Scientific Examination of Documents: Methods
and Techniques*
D. Ellen
(CRC Press, 2006)

Scientific Examination of Questioned Documents
J. S. Kelly & B. S. Lindblom
(CRC Press 2006, 2nd edn)

Stable Isotope Forensics: Methods and Forensic Applications of Stable Isotope Analysis
W. Meier-Augenstein
(Wiley Online Library, 2nd edn 2017)

ORGANIZATIONS & WEBSITES

LEVERHULME TRUST ————

In 2016 the Leverhulme Trust awarded £10 million to Professors Sue Black and Niamh Nic Daéid. This is the largest research grant ever awarded in forensic science in the UK and it established the Leverhulme Research Centre for Forensic Science (LRCFS) at the University of Dundee, Scotland. The aim of LRCFS is to develop the underpinning scientific confidence in forensic evidence, where needed, for the Judiciary and the juries in the service of justice.
www.leverhulme.ac.uk

AAFS (American Academy of Forensic Sciences)
www.aafs.org

AAFS (Australian Academy of Forensic Sciences)
www.forensicacademy.org

CAHID (Centre for Anatomy & Human Identification), University of Dundee
www.cahid.dundee.ac.uk

ENFSI (European Network of Forensic Science Institutes) Tasked with improving the mutual exchange of information in the field of forensic science
www.enfsi.eu

GIFT-CBRN (Generic Integrated Forensic Toolbox to investigate Chemical, Biological, Radiological and Nuclear incidents) Procedures, practices and guidelines for CBRN defence
www.giftforensics.eu

LRCFS (Leverhulme Research Centre for Forensic Science)
www.dundee.ac.uk/leverhulme

NIST (National Institute of Standards and Technology), US Department of Commerce
www.nist.gov

RAI (Royal Anthropological Institute)
www.therai.org.uk

SEFARI Gateway (Scottish Environment, Food and Agriculture Research Institutes) Strategic environmental assessment programme
www.gov.scot/topics/environment/environmental-assessment/sea

EDITORS

Sue Black is a forensic anthropologist and a human anatomist. She is Director of both the Centre for Anatomy & Human Identification (CAHID) and the Leverhulme Research Centre for Forensic Science at the University of Dundee. She is a Dame Commander of the British Empire, a life-long Professor of Anatomy for the Royal Scottish Academy and a fellow of four other royal academies. Professor Black was also awarded an OBE in 2001 and holds two police commendations for her forensic casework.

Niamh Nic Daéid is an award-winning chartered chemist and a forensic chemist. She is Director of both the Centre for Excellence for New Psychoactive Substances Research and the Leverhulme Research Centre for Forensic Science at the University of Dundee. She is also research lead for the Centre for Anatomy & Human Identification at Dundee. Her forensic expertise is primarily in fire investigation and drug chemistry. She is a Fellow of the Royal Society of Edinburgh and also a fellow of five other royal academies and professional bodies.

FOREWORD

Val McDermid is a top-selling crime writer whose work has been translated into more than thirty languages. She graduated from Oxford and worked as a journalist for 16 years before turning to write fiction. Hailed by *The Independent* as the 'queen of crime' she is the recipient of numerous international awards including, in 2011, the Lambda Literary Foundation Pioneer Award.

CONTRIBUTORS

Mike Allen has had a career in forensic document examination that spans thirty years. He has helped to train and educate new examiners from around the world and to set standards in the specialty. He gave the handwriting evidence at the trial of Dr Harold Shipman in 1999.

Christophe Champod has an MSc and a PhD in forensic science from the University of Lausanne. From 1999 to 2003, he led the UK's Interpretation Research Group of the Forensic Science Service before taking up full professorship at Lausanne's School of Criminal Justice where he also manages the accredited forensic laboratory. In 2015 he received the ENFSI (European Network of Forensic Science Institutes) Distinguished Scientist Award. His research is devoted to the inferential aspects of forensic identification techniques, areas in which he acts as an expert witness.

Lorna Dawson is head of forensic soil science at the James Hutton Institute in Dundee and visiting professor of forensic science at Robert Gordon University in Aberdeen. She is a registered expert with the UK's National Crime Agency and regularly takes part in training police and forensic practitioners worldwide. She holds diplomas in civil and criminal law and serves as an expert witness on many high-profile cases. She sits on the British Association of Science General Committee, and is a member of the ASPT (Animals, Soil, Plant Trace) working group of ENFSI.

Zeno Geradts is a senior forensic scientist in the department of digital and biometric traces at the Netherlands Forensic Institute and professor of forensic data science at the University of Amsterdam. He is active in the European Forensic network as chairman of the Forensic IT working group and was nominated as President-Elect at the American Academy of Forensic Sciences.

Lucina Hackman is a senior lecturer in human identification at CAHID in Dundee, specializing in analysing images for age estimation and other forensic anthropological analyses. She is a case-active forensic anthropologist accredited by the Royal Anthropological Institute and a registered expert practitioner on the forensic expert database of the National Crime Agency. Dr Hackman's expertise has been used in cases of murder, missing persons investigations, trafficking, paedophilic, child abuse and terrorist incidents.

Adrian Linacre has a degree in zoology and a PhD in molecular genetics. He entered forensic science in 1994 and, in 2010, became the inaugural South Australia Justice Chair in Forensic Science & Emerging DNA Technology at Flinders University. He has published more than 140 papers in peer-reviewed journals and is co-author of *An Introduction to Forensic Genetics*, editor of *Forensic Science in Wildlife Investigations*, and Associate Editor of *Forensic Science International Genetics.* Professor Linacre was Chair of 25th Congress of the International Society for Forensic Genetics (ISFG) and was elected National President of the Australian & New Zealand Forensic Science Society in 2018.

Craig McKenzie is a senior lecturer in forensic chemistry and co-director of the Centre for Excellence in New Psychoactive Substances Research at the University of Dundee. He is a former reporting forensic chemist, specializing in drugs, general chemistry and quality assurance. Dr McKenzie started his career as an environmental chemist and toxicologist studying the effects of pollution on marine mammals.

Paul Reedy was Coordinator Digital Evidence, and Manager Forensic Operations with the Australian Federal Police; and Manager Digital Evidence with the Department of Forensic Sciences in Washington DC. He is a member of the Organising Committee for the Interpol International Forensic Science Managers Symposium, and a member of the Digital Evidence Sub-Committee for the Organization of Scientific Area Committees of NIST.

Chris Rynn is the course coordinator for the MSc Forensic Art and Facial Identification at the University of Dundee. His background in human anatomy and medical art led on to research in forensic facial reconstruction. Dr Rynn has worked with the UK police, the FBI (USA), BKA (Germany), the SAPS (South Africa) and Interpol.

Diana Swales has an MSc and a PhD in human osteology and funerary archaeology from the University of Sheffield. She is a lecturer and practitioner at CAHID in Dundee. She is an osteoarchaeologist and archaeologist with expertise in the excavation and post-excavation analysis of human skeletal remains from archaeological sites, and teaches human osteology, paleopathology and burial archaeology in both commercial and academic institutions. Dr Swales is a Member of the Chartered Institute for Archaeologists and Fellow of the Society of Antiquaries and Royal Anthropological Institute.

Grant Thomson is a qualified forensic practitioner with more than twenty years of experience in the criminal justice arena. As an Authorised Forensic Scientist, he conducted firearm and tool mark analysis for more than ten years and is currently researching the morphology of cut marks on bone in relation to criminal dismemberment.

INDEX

ACKNOWLEDGEMENTS

EDITORS' ACKNOWLEDGEMENTS
No book is written in isolation. We extend our gratitude to every contributor for helping us to bring this text together at very short notice and hope that they are as delighted with the final product as we are. But the text is only one half and the beautiful illustrations seen here are entirely the result of the exceptional skills of Nicky Ackland-Snow. Every book has a team that makes it happen and this would never have been achieved without the incredible talents and patience of Stephanie Evans, senior project editor for Ivy Press. She has been such a delight to work with and a consummate professional. Huge thanks also to Jane Roe, our copy editor, and Jenny Campbell, assistant editor. The design and production teams made this such a painless process and we are indebted to them.

PICTURE CREDITS
The publisher would like to thank the following for permission to reproduce copyright material. All reasonable efforts have been made to trace copyright holders and to obtain their permission for the use of copyright material. The publisher apologizes for any errors or omissions and will gratefully incorporate any corrections in future reprints if notified.

Alamy/Paul Fern: 39CL; David R. Frazier Photolibrary, Inc: 69C; Mirrorpix: 20; Science History Images: 126. Clipart.com: 103C, 105TL, 139BR, 143R. Dartmouth College Electron Microscope Facility: 107. École des Sciences Criminelles, Université de Lausanne, Switzerland: 81BL, 81C, 81(BG). Getty Images/Bettmann: 62; Georges De Keerle: 42; Heritage Images: 93CR; Pasieka: 45TR; Transcendental Graphics: 41L; WPA Pool: 144. Library of Congress, Washington DC: 41R. Missouri Botanical Gardens: 93CR, 101CL. The New York Public Library: 139TC. © Christopher Rynn: 25. Science Photo Library/GiPhotoStock: 71BL; Ted Kinsman: 69TR; Herra Kuulapaa—Precires: 69C; Andrew Lambert Photography: 71BL; Matteis/Look at Sciences: 69TR. Shutterstock: 111TC; 24 Novembers: 129C; aarrows: 121TC; acceptphoto: 61; addkm: 143CR; Adrian Niederhaeuser: 147CR; Africa Studio: 29, 133CR; Aha-Soft: 107BC; Alberto Tirado: 105CR; Alex Mit: 27C; Alex Tihonovs: 89TL; Alexander Gold: 59C; Alhovik: 149BR; Allusioni: 50(BG); AnartStock: 131BC; andreiuc88: 131(BG); Andrey_Kuzmin: 27B; Anton-Burakov: 113C; arda savasciogullari: 29; Arkadiusz Fajer: 143TR; Arkady Mazor: 151C; art4all: 123L, 123R; Artistdesign13: 133BC; AVIcon: 129BL, 129C; Axro: 121CL; Ayzek: 133CR; Barbol: 59BC; Bearacreative: 107CR; Bergamont: 123BL, 123BR; Betacam-SP: 87C; Boreala: 105TR; Casther: 71TL; Cbenjasuwan: 69C; Channarong Pherngjanda: 29CL; charles taylor: 89BR; Christophe Rolland: 115C; Cioki: 91BC; cla78: 17(BG); Claudio Divizia: 77C; Coloa Studio: 93CR; Couperfield: 103BC; David Benton: 133C; Digital Genetics: 39CL; Dmitry Bodyaev: 113BC; Donflore: 125BR; Donikz: 151C; Dragan Milovanovic: 57C; Dragance137: 17; Dramaj: 141B; echo3005: 89BR; eddo: 139TC; Eliks: 95C, 123TR; Elina Li: 87C; Elzbieta Sekowska: 107C; Eremin Sergey: 71B; Erik Svoboda:

65C; Everett Collection: 39CR, 50CL, 77BR, 121CL, 123BC, 123CR, 123(BG), 139BR, 139CL, 143BR; Exopixel: 89BL; ; Ezepov Dmitry: 95C; Fabio Berti: 131C; Fabrai: 147CL; FabrikaSimf: 139C; Fineart1: 29; Flutes: 23C; Forance: 103BC; Fotorawin: 113CR; Foxie: 115(BG); FreddEP: 57C; Freedom Studio: 69; galimovma79: 65BC; Garvan333: 111; Golden Shrimp: 51(BG); Gordan: 57C; gritsalak karalak: 95CB, 115C; Hein Nouwens: 31B, 103C, 115BC; Hernie Briedenhann: 27BR; HolyCrazyLazy: 31B; Humdan: 69(BG); Iakov Kalinin: 147C; Idambies: 149C; Igorsky: 103B; Illustration Projects: 149C; Ilolab: 61C; Imagehub: 91BC; Ink Drop: 121TL; Inked Pixels: 61C; InnervisionArt: 49CR; Iresoo3: 89CR; Ivan Popovych: 77C; Jade ThaiCatwalk: 151BR; Jarva Jar: 23BL; Jason Salmon: 89CR; Jiri Hera: 133C; Jose Luis Calvo: 59C; Joshua Rainey Photography: 89CL; Jowait: 87B; JoyImage: 91C; Juan J. Jimenez: 61TC; Jubal Harshaw: 61T; Jueurgen Faelcle: 49CL; Juli Hansen: 111TC; Jumpingsack: 27T; Kaesler Media: 31CR; Kalewa: 23CR; Kamenetskiy Konstantin: 81L; Karen Perhus: 151C; Keantian: 65B; Keith Wheatley: 111BL; Ket4up: 125TR; Khuruzero: 77C; Kimree: 105TL; KN: 45C; koya979: 41CL; Krailurk Warasup: 129C; Krasovski Dmitri: 113(BG); Larysa Ray: 39CL; Lebendkulturen.de: 107C; Lenor Ko: 71BL; Leonid Andronov: 91CR; Lev Kroptov: 125CR; Line Icons: 123TR; LuFeeTheBear: 111C; Lukiyanova Natalia frenta: 29TC; Lynea: 29CR; Magnetix: 131TC; Majeczka: 129TR; Marcel Derweduwen: 23CR; Marco Rosales: 50(BG); Markovka: 71TL; Maryna Stamatova: 49BC; Matej Kotula: 103C; Matsabe: 95BR; Maxx-Studio: 133C; Mega Pixel: 65C; Mikhail Pogosov: 133C; molekuul_be: 95CR; monbibi: 151TR; Monika Beitlova: 149B; Morphart Creation: 49C, 59BR, 69TC; Mr. Rawin Tanpin:: 111B; MrVander: 17B; Newelle: 41BL; Nik Merkulov: 111BR; NikomMaelao Production: 65C; Nishihama: 81(BG); Nobeatsofierce: 113TR; Nobuhiro Asada: 147CL; Nomad_Soul: 57; Nyvit-art: 105C; Oleg Golovnev: 89BL; olga n zelenkova: 131T; oneo: 79C; Pakhnyushchy: 27BL; Pakpoom Nunjul: 113C; Pashabo: 50(BG); Pavalena: 107(BG); Petukhov Anton: 151C; phenyx7776: 23TR; Picsfive: 61C; Plutonian: 105BL; Pogonici: 27C; Protasov AN: 103C, 103TR; Puwadol Jaturawutthichal: 23CL; railway fx: 101CR; rcarter: 77T; Robert Lucian Crusitu: 129C; Robian: 91CR; Roman Nerud: 87CR; Runrun2: 57CR; Saknakorn: 45TR; Samarets: 123BC; Samolevsky: 115C; sar14ev: 59C; schankz: 27BC; science photo: 71BR; Scisetti Alfio: 50(BG); Seenerg: 129CL; Sergieiev: 89BR; SkillUp: 129CB; Skockp: 149BC; Somchai Som: 133CL; Sonate: 133C; Spantomoda: 123C; st.noon: 71BC; stefanocapra: 41B(BG); Stephen Rees: 87TC; steve estvanik: 15CL; Stockforlife: 133C; Stockish: 141; StockVector: 143CL; successo images: 113BC; sumstock: 141C; SuriyaPhoto: 87TL; Susan Law Cain: 41C(BG); Swill Klitch: 61C; Tairy Greene: 41CR; Tanyastock: 141; Tarzhanova: 141T; Tefi: 17; Tewan Banditrukkanka: 17C; Thomas Hecker: 77T; Tobijah: 57BR; Torin55: 149CL; Tovovan: 121C; Tridsanu Thopet: 23TL; Triff: 149C; Trisanu Thopet: 17BR; Urfin: 113BR; Vadim Petrakov: 131T; Vandathal: 71TR; Vector Market: 105TR; Veronika M: 87C; vesna cvorovic: 149C; ViKiVector: 105(BG); Vitaly Korovin: 151C; VitaminCo: 133CR; Voyagerix: 141BL; vs148: 49C; Web-Design: 133T; Wellphoto: 29CR; wk1003mike: 89TR; wolfman57: 93TL; xpixel: 141T; Yai Studio: 113BC; Yarbsontan Nionadr: 29BC; Yasbrand Cosjin: 81B; Yuravector: 27T; Yuri Samsonov: 45BR; Zerbor: 103B; Ziviani: 91T; Zoltan Pataki: 151C. University of Dundee. Reproduced with the permission of University of Dundee Archive Services: 108. US National Library of Medicine: 107T. Wellcome Library, London: 23CL, 29BC, 45T, 50TR, 57CL, 84, 91BC, 91C. Wikimedia Commons/Frettie: 39CR.